She Said
He Said
I Said

NEW WRITING SCOTLAND 35

Edited by
Diana Hendry
and
Susie Maguire

Gaelic adviser:
Rody Gorman

Association for Scottish Literary Studies

Association for Scottish Literary Studies
Scottish Literature, 7 University Gardens
University of Glasgow, Glasgow G12 8QH
www.asls.org.uk

ASLS is a registered charity no. SC006535

First published 2017

British Library Cataloguing in Publication Data

A CIP record for this book is available
from the British Library

ISBN 978-1-906841-30-0

The Association for Scottish Literary Studies
acknowledges the support of Creative Scotland
towards the publication of this book

Printed by Bell & Bain Ltd, Glasgow

CONTENTS

INTRODUCTION

This issue of *New Writing Scotland* welcomes Susie Maguire as the new co-editor after Gerry Cambridge. Susie has published two collections of short stories (*Furthermore* and *The Short Hello*) and has edited four anthologies. Many of her stories have been broadcast on BBC Radio 4 and Radio Scotland. Through the SOA Susie's done a lot to keep short stories on the BBC's agenda. Her first poetry pamphlet, *How to Hug*, came out in 2009.

So, Susie's first co-editing year and my third and last. The large boxes that occupy my very small study for at least six months of the year and which are labelled **YES NO MAYBE** have been packed away under the bed. It occurs to me that Sylvia Dow, who wrote the mysterious and alarming title story, *She Said: He Said: I Said*, might like to try her hand at a *Yes: No: Maybe* story.

It is always the Maybes that give me the most heartache. I think I might be a natural Maybe myself. The poems and stories that go into the Maybe Box go there reluctantly and only after I've read them several times. When Susie and I get to share our shortlists, I'm cheered when Susie pulls out something that for me was a *maybe* and which, after we've talked it over, turns into a *yes*.

This being my last year on the two-seater editorial sofa, I thought I might indulge in a little retrospective view of *New Writing Scotland*. My partner, Hamish Whyte, has co-edited a grand total of nine NWSs. He has the collection. *New Writing Scotland 2* (1984) was the first to have an introduction. The editors (Alexander Scott and James Aitchison) issued the reminder that ASLS had designed the anthology 'as a vehicle for new writing rather than new writers'. I believe the anthology to be equally important to both new and established writers and that it is this mix that has made *New Writing Scotland* both successful and long lasting. Looking at the biographical notes for *New Writing Scotland 2*, it brought a smile to read that Ian Rankin's 'first novel is now seeking a publisher'.

We received submissions from nearly five hundred writers this year. I aim at a 'yes' short list of thirty-plus and a 'maybe' list of about the same. Apart from the editors finding agreement, there are other choices to be made that govern the final selection. Is there a fair gender balance? A balance between poetry and prose? And last but far from least, there's that most important person, The Reader, to consider. One wants an anthology to have its own identity, to have variety, to include both the lyrical, the dramatic and the humorous. I hope we have succeeded.

Last year's *New Writing Scotland* seemed slightly obsessed with sheep. There's much more of a menagerie in this issue – Jim Carruth's 'Macintyre's Big Horse', Rose McDonagh's 'Owlets', Lydia Harris's utterly lovely 'Goat: an Assay' (with ears that 'old women in scarves finger . . . as if they were spindles'); Sarah Isaac's dramatic and unexpected 'Stalking Deer', Graeme Stones's 'Sperm Whale Ashore' and Anna Crowe's beautifully described museum exhibit *Regalecus banksii*.

As always, the anthology is arranged alphabetically by author. Two things are particularly pleasing this year. The first is the long poem by Mandy Haggith, 'Alphabet', that encompasses observations, memories and thoughts using the alphabet itself as a kind of prompt. And secondly, by chance or some kind of literary synchronicity, the last item in the anthology is John Young's 'My Wee Buik o Genesis'.

It's been a pleasure and a privilege to be one of the many writers who have edited *New Writing Scotland*.

Diana Hendry

NEW WRITING SCOTLAND 36: SUBMISSION INSTRUCTIONS

The thirty-sixth volume of *New Writing Scotland* will be published in summer 2018. Submissions are invited from writers resident in Scotland or Scots by birth, upbringing or inclination. All forms of writing are welcome: autobiography and memoirs; creative responses to events and experiences; drama; graphic artwork (monochrome only); poetry; political and cultural commentary and satire; short fiction; travel writing or any other creative prose may be submitted, but not full-length plays or novels, though self-contained extracts are acceptable. The work must not be previously published, submitted, or accepted for publication elsewhere, and may be in any of the languages of Scotland.

Submissions should be typed on one side of the paper only and the sheets secured at the top left corner. Prose pieces should be double-spaced and carry an approximate word-count. **You should provide a covering letter, clearly marked with your name and address.** *Please also put your name on the individual works.* If you would like to receive an acknowledgement of receipt of your manuscript, please enclose a stamped addressed postcard. If you would like to be informed if your submission is unsuccessful, or would like your submissions returned, you should enclose a stamped addressed envelope with sufficient postage. Submissions should be sent by **30 September 2017**, in an A4 envelope, to the address below. We are sorry but we cannot accept submissions by fax or email.

Please be aware that we have limited space in each edition, and therefore shorter pieces are more suitable – although longer items of exceptional quality may still be included. **Please send no more than four poems, or one prose work**. Successful contributors will be paid at the rate of £20 per published page. Authors retain all rights to their work(s), and are free to submit and/or publish the same work(s) elsewhere after they appear in *New Writing Scotland*.

ASLS
Scottish Literature
7 University Gardens
University of Glasgow
Glasgow G12 8QH, Scotland
Tel +44 (0)141 330 5309
www.asls.org.uk

Viccy Adams

PERFORMANCE

Mother has this thing – this ongoing joke with me – that if she gets to be what she calls a burden, especially as a result of the loss of her mental faculties, then I am to take immediate steps, to respond directly and without hesitation.

'Take a shotgun, darling.' She raises her eyebrows and looks off to one side at this point, usually to stop the cigarette smoke from tearing her up and impacting on her mascara. 'Take me by the arm and lead me down to the end of the garden. Then—' she points her fingers dramatically to the side of her own head and clicks her tongue.

Today her audience is the postman, who she has inveigled in for a cup of tea under the pretext of needing to find her glasses before signing for a package. The two of them sit at the half-laid tea table while I finish wiping surfaces and fluster, one eye on the wall clock.

'I don't have a shotgun,' I remind her, struggling with the lid of a jar of jam then ending up giving it to the postie instead.

'That's your Christmas sorted then,' he jokes.

I try to move the koala toy back into Mother's room and she fusses until I put it back on the sideboard. 'That's a little present from Australia,' she says, as if the postie had asked her about it. 'They're making a documentary about me.'

'If they can find the footage,' I remind her. 'It's been six months.'

Mother pushes back from the table to check which dish I'm using for the clotted cream. 'You must think so badly of us,' she confides to her audience. 'Serving you *shop-bought* scones.' She drops her voice for shop-bought, makes a face.

Postie isn't paying attention to what she's saying but that's okay because he's looking at the photos of her on the walls and making all the right noises. 'That's never you there, is it?'

Mother folds her hands demurely on top of the rug over her lap and pretends to be modest. 'I started training when I was five, but of course I'd been dancing since I could walk.'

That's a lie, actually. She started classes when she was four, according to the certificates she keeps hidden upstairs because of the incriminating dates on them. And, by her sister's account, she wasn't reckoned anything special until what my aunt calls her blossoming talents caught the attention of a stage manager during a day trip to London that turned into an overnight stay and ended in a contract.

'My parents couldn't stand to see a daughter of theirs on the stage so I ran away from home aged fourteen. I've only ever felt truly alive when I'm dancing.'

Postie doesn't know what to say to this. He avoids both our eyes, finishes his cuppa in a gulp and refuses a second scone. I can sense him trying not to stare at her legs. He's backing out the door and Mother is still trilling on about the names and places and faces she's danced with and in and for.

'What a nice man,' she breaks the silence after the click of the Yale lock. 'I think he rather took a shine to me.'

I clear his setting and lay a fresh one. No comment.

'Just as well you were here.' She wheels herself over to the strategically lowered hallway mirror to check her lipstick and adjust a hairpin. 'Fancy needing a chaperone at my age.'

*

The interviewer turns up bang on the strike of three. Mother introduces me as her live-in carer, and laughs until the woman joins in.

'I'm her daughter,' I explain. 'But I do live here.' We've agreed Mother will stay in her chair for this one but I don't trust her to keep to that so I'm stuck in all afternoon too.

The woman asks if I also danced professionally, eyeing the width of my body dubiously. Before I can answer her Mother starts in with *Jessica and I have an agreement*. So I busy myself with pulling curtains into place until the click of Mother's tongue signifies the end.

This interviewer is particularly interested in Mother's childhood. After tea I wheel Mother – too tired to put up a fight – into the other room and begin laying out the photos she has pre-approved for publication. They cover the wide expanse of pine with black, white and sepia memories, fading into tints of colour at the far end. Like the framed ones on the walls they are all of Mother on stage or at press events. A consummate professional in endless variations of leotards and smart hats.

'It's the performer in the person that makes them stand out,' Mother is saying. 'I took Jessica to see Fonteyn and Nureyev at the Kings when they were quite old. Just a selection of set pieces, Romeo and Juliet, that kind of thing. And you know what she did afterwards?'

The interviewer indicates that no, she has no idea. Her notebook is closed: she's not interested in anecdotes from my childhood.

'She wept. She said it put her heart to shame – can't have been more than eight or nine at the time – that there wasn't enough soul in her to give over to produce something like that. Not the way they did. Still,' Mother sips her water and grimaces at the bitter, chalky taste of the painkillers stirred into it. 'We aren't all born to be exceptional.'

*

It was my aunt who took me to classes. Sometimes my father, sometimes my granny, but mainly my aunt. At first Mother was kept away by circumstances – touring in term times. But then she heard I had no particular aptitude and said it might be kinder if the school didn't make an association between us. It helped that my mother danced under her maiden name but the staff still knew who I was, of course. They sent me home with letters begging items for charity auctions, the occasional introduction to patrons. In the classes themselves there was no escaping the trap of my father's family's broad, hammy physique and short legs, accompanied by moues of frustration from the teachers as they battled to make me pirouette with stability, clean-up my *enchaînement* or elevate my knees.

The dance school took us en masse to anything worth the minibus, a regular parade of Coppelias, Swan Lakes, Giselles and the occasional more daring production that only the older girls were eligible for, due to (whispers) the content. While we crowded on the pavement by the hall the classes were held in, chattering loudly to cover the rustle of forbidden sweets in our pockets, we'd be issued with mohair stoles – left over from some long-past show – as an outing uniform. As we left in the minibus the Director would spray us all with perfume: twenty-odd girls with headache-inducing buns and patent sandals, reeking of white musk.

When the lights went out for curtain up us girls would reach across the row and hold each other's hands because of the excitement. On the rare occasions my mother toured the provinces and performed nearby, the massed hysteria would reach fever pitch. I'd be so exhausted by the interval that it was all I could do to sit upright and weep; no chance of picking my way to the foyer. One of the other girls would get my tub of strawberry ice-cream instead, spoon it into her satisfied mouth with the wooden spoon so cunningly hidden in the lid. Then at the end of the performance the Director would stand there, eying the snotty, red-eyed puddle in front of her and repeating *you're sure you don't want to go backstage and say hello?*

The mohair stoles picked up fleas one year. Or lice. I can't remember exactly, just that they had to be burnt and were never replaced. By the time I was eligible to be brought to the more interesting productions, that sense of being part of something had gone along with the patent-leather sandals and the perfume.

I quit dancing about then. Joined a choral group and chewed gum and cut my hair too short for a bun, wore heels high enough to break ankles.

*

After the interviewer leaves Mother refuses to let me use the winch for her afternoon nap. 'You should go out,' she says. 'No need for both of us to stay in all the time. Or at least open a window for me. Fresh air's better for my health than all this bloody central heating, darling.'

She broods over an emptying packet of Marlboro Reds and tells me to leave those photos where they are on the dining room table. 'I'll try not to shed dust on them,' she snaps. 'So sorry to inconvenience your catalogue of my legacy.'

*

We eat our dinner in front of the television, on laptrays. 'That Bussell woman's a giant,' Mother sniffs. 'But at least she knows how to talk to performers. Not like that orange one. I've met enough of his type. Don't you talk to me about choreographers.'

I chase a final pea through a slick of gravy then suggest putting the radio on instead.

'Nonsense,' Mother says. 'If I didn't want to watch it all I have to do is use the remote. I can reach things, Jessica. It's not time for the shotgun yet.' She looks around expectantly for an audience. The phone goes – a woman with a thick Australian accent who asks for Mother by her stage name.

Leaving the doors open in case she needs me, I move out of the room to give them privacy. But not before catching her regaling whoever it is with *I was just saying to my Jessica. When the time comes you're to take me by the arm—*

*

The new delivery of pills is still in the white paper bag, waiting to be divvied up into the day-labelled plastic snap-case. While I portion them out – one and a half of the white, one blue, two orange, a dark red on alternate days – I can see my reflection in the steamed-up kitchen window.

The spare half pills go with the others in the tin matryoshka tea caddy left over from Mother's guest spot with the Bolshoi; the back of the head has a latch that lifts up, just long enough to store a measuring spoon for the loose tea inside. You'd never guess it was there unless you knew to look for it. The caddy itself goes at the back of the tea cupboard, the wide painted eyes peeking over the tops of the matching Denby mugs.

I imagine how heavy a shotgun would be, the kick in the shoulder from pulling the trigger. Compassion, removing a burden.

The click of Mother's tongue is followed quickly by the click of the handset.

'Fancy that,' she calls through, revived. 'They've found the footage. They do want to fly me over after all. Or fly someone over here.

The girl was scant on the details, Jessica, but she'll email you to sort it out.'

'Australia?' I give her the row of conjoined plastic cases, celled by morning and night.

'I toured there. You were, oh, ten? Eleven?'

'Eleven,' I agree. Actually I was thirteen. I got my first period the day after she left.

'I held a koala.' She examines the pills in her hand. 'This all?'

'I can call the pharmacist again if you want the prescription checked?'

'No need.' She swallows. 'Smelly creatures, koalas. Sharp, dirty little claws.'

'They look so needy.' I take the snap-case back, check the lids are all tight.

'Everyone thinks they're cute but up close they're nothing special. They just cling.' She's slurring now, slightly. I take her tray and wheel her to her room, rolling my shoulders to loosen them. Even with the winch there should be two people to get her into bed. Mother did not take to the night assistant we trialled earlier in the year. The agency has refused to send anyone else.

'It wasn't easy for me either.' She whispers it. 'Standing out.'

But I'm not sure I've heard right.

*

The Australian calls back, actually, rather than emailing. She's studying in London, wants to come and film Mother. There's no question of us going to Australia.

'I want to capture her movements in old age,' she says. 'Now we have the documentary footage to compare it to.'

Mother hasn't told her she's in a wheelchair, of course. 'She doesn't move,' I explain. But the researcher is a bit of a bitch.

'She still moves,' she insists, over the phone. 'That's not a problem.'

Then when she arrives she wants to take Mother out. Out of the flat.

'We don't do that,' I tell her.

'Nonsense,' Mother says. 'Jessica, get my coat.'

She doesn't have a coat. Hasn't needed one for years. I fetch her one of mine and the two of them eye it like there's a smell in the room.

'We could go to the shops,' the Australian says. She's shorter than me, petite. Hair scraped back into a bun. She moves in quick darts. Pointy nose, elbows, thin lips. Pale. I thought all Australians had amazing suntans.

'Not me,' she says. 'I spend all my time indoors, in class.'

Mother nods vigorously. I put the coat back in the closet and the Australian girl arranges a rug around Mother's shoulders, like a huge shawl.

After they've begun manoeuvring down the stairs I stand inside our flat with my back to the front door, breathing in the emptiness. *We could go to the shops.* By the time I rejoin them they're already halfway down the garden.

The Australian has two helpers with her. Burly men who express themselves in grunts and carry all the equipment, including Mother in her chair. Near the end of the garden the three strangers kick the leaves about and pretend to fall over. Mother laughs and she tells them about her death plan.

'Don't film that,' I say. 'That's private.' But nobody pays attention to me.

'Circle your wrists for me.' The Australian puts Mother through her paces, unwinding her from the rug to raise and lower her shoulders, kneeling in the wet leaves to remove her slippers.

'I can do that,' I say. 'Let me hold those.'

It's only a matter of time before Mother announces she'd be fine to stand, for a bit. I go back inside to fetch her frame but when I return she's suspended between the two burly men, feet inches from the ground.

'She bruises easily,' I say. 'Be careful.'

She insists on being carried right down to the very end, where the horse chestnut tree stands. 'Are there any conkers left?' she asks, and the Australian girl does a closeup on Mother's ankles, tells her to think of today as a rehearsal and relax into it.

I stand to the side, shoes slick from the overgrown grass, trying to make them take more care. *It's cold out here. Those leaves are slippery. Don't exhaust her.* One of the burly men shushes me, gesturing to the long microphone Mother and the Australian are cooing into.

They film for what feels like hours. Mother chatters away the whole time, tiring herself out and showing off. The hem of her trousers is soaked through. Finally the Australian takes her arm and helps her stand up, for a moment, before the men take over and lower her back into the chair. 'Thank you,' she says to Mother. 'That was beautiful.'

'We'll need to change you,' I say and they both look at me blankly. 'Your clothes. You can't sit in wet clothes.'

Mother sniffs. 'No need to shout. I'm not deaf.' The men begin manoeuvring her and the chair back up the garden.

'You must be so proud.' The Australian turns her camera off and walks next to me.

'She was a magnificent dancer,' I say. 'I saw her—'

'Not then,' she interrupts, pulling at my lapel with her tiny, pale hand. 'Not then.'

*

Before the Australian leaves – far too late in the evening – Mother tells her that being around her makes her feel young and they hug. They make plans for the rest of the week. I wait in the kitchen, door half-shut, only the under-counter lights on. I watch the closed door of the tea cupboard until the front door clicks shut. I'm about to change my mind when Mother calls through asking for a glass of water rather than her usual small tumbler of sherry. 'Must stay hydrated, darling. Big day tomorrow. Cheryl really is quite something, isn't she? So sparky.'

I pour two glasses of water and get the matryoshka tea caddy out from the back of the cupboard. I tip the hoarded contents entirely into one of the glasses and stir until it isn't cloudy any more.

*

Mother picks the remote up and puts on a repeat of *Strictly*. I place the call button on the coffee table by her chair, carefully, and sit back in my armchair.

The judges hold up their scores. 'That's unfortunate. She's a natural soloist but she couldn't do that routine without him to lean on. He's worth more than that.'

I can't make out which celebrity she's talking about.

'You're worth more than that,' she repeats. 'You were more than that.' Mother is talking to Darcy now. 'You've got the wrong arms, darling.'

I sip my water and grimace. I can hear her telling me the same thing when I show her that picture from my Christmas show. I remind her about it but she says it wasn't like that.

'What was it like then?'

Turning the volume down, Mother tuts at the television. 'Interpretation,' she says. 'Arms are for translating the emotion of the piece, characterisation.'

'I was a tree.'

She laughs and mutters something about being wooden. Then she sighs. 'You were more than that – your part meant more than that. Everyone has their role.' She fiddles with the buttons on the remote, raising the music back up as the next showstopper begins. The faces of the performers blur and spin. I drain the rest of my glass and think about the piles of wet leaves scattered at the end of the garden. I picture the horse chestnut tree and think of arms reaching out like branches, vital and strong.

Jane Aldous

WASHERWOMEN ON CALTON HILL

Washerwomen on Calton Hill, calotype by
Thomas Begbie 1887

Scunnered. Such a good day
for drying clothes up on the hill, away
from all the smoky lums and up he comes,
wants us to pose on the slopes.
The cheek of him, we were all in position,
standing, kneeling and his box on legs all set up,
when he asked us to wait while he runs down to the gorse
to relieve himself!
Eventually he flitted with all his stuff.
Then one day when I was rushing down Leith Street,
I noticed a picture in the studio window.
I was taken aback by my dark shawl blurred by the breeze,
all the clothes laid on the grass, our white bonnets,
             long dark dresses,
the bairns' tresses and how that Thomas Begbie had
             made us look
like ourselves but more elegant and had squeezed us all
out of his box on to one small, square of paper.

Jennifer M. Baker

RAIN

The fetching of water was always the girl's first chore. Ironically, the rain was sloshing down the tiny windows of the croft house and gurgling into the barrels but that stuff was no use for drinking. Her mother was already stoking the fire. The kettle, with the last of yesterday's water in it, was beginning to boil. There'd be a hot cup of tea waiting for her when she got back. Her mother moved slowly back and forth in the kitchen doing all the morning things. No words were spoken but her ma's great smile warmed her as she slogged up across the hill with the two buckets, her wet pigtails making dark smears across the back of her oilskin. She placed the buckets under the spring waiting for them to fill. She thought about the books she'd read which told of houses on the mainland with water that spouted out of a pipe inside the house whenever the tap was turned on. People here on the island said it was such a luxury and she tried to imagine the comfort of it, but couldn't. She thought of water spilling all over the floor; of uncontrollable gushes that would soak everything in the house. Oh no – it wasn't possible. Even the wet tramped in with boots or the gusts that blew through the door in the winter gales made enough mess. Imagine what a flowing tap would do. Water from the spring must be better. It was right out of the way of the house and could do no damage.

She stood in the rain whilst the gin-clear water gushed into the tin pail and splashed over the dark blue rocks of the spring. Her father had placed a board held down with stones over the spring pool 'To keep the water good,' he said. But he said *uisge* which sounds like the sound of water. He used to say that Gaelic is the language for all things to do with the earth. He said that English is just not up to it although she had to speak English at school or Mr Morrison would hit them with the tawse. She liked school. She was good at the work. Mr Morrison said that she was a scholar. John and she were the best. John's mother once told her that her hair was like the raven's wing and one sunny day, as they sat by the side of the loch,

John looked at it closely and said very seriously that he knew exactly what his mother meant when she said the raven's wing. She liked when John spoke like that. The priest said that one day John would be the island bard as his grandfather had been before him.

She thought of all these things as she waited for the pails to fill. She liked going to the spring. Especially on days like that day. Days when the island seemed to sink deeper into the loch under the weight of the heavy clouds and the insistent rain came down on the earth like smoke and the scent of it filled her mind. She liked it because it gave her time to think. The rain had the power to entrance her like the spells of the witches who had lived here long ago and, for all she knew, still did. The softness of it would caress the skin of her face and the swirls of it in front of her eyes made her dreamy and light and then she would reach out to new horizons way beyond the loch and the mountains only half visible and veiled in ancient mystery.

Fetching the water gave her time to think of things like the way they spoke at home and the way they had to speak at school. She wondered whether they talked in two ways in other countries. She knew it didn't happen in England because her favourite author was Enid Blyton and so she knew what happened down there. They all spoke the same language. She thought about places like France. She knew very little about there. Perhaps it was the same as here. Perhaps it was only in England that they didn't have to learn two languages because they already spoke English. Probably every other country had to speak English at school.

She thought a lot about her family. About her father and three older brothers who worked all day and every day – even on Sunday although Mr Morrison said in class that it was a sin to work on the Sabbath. She told her father this in case he didn't know and went to hell by accident but he told her to tell Mr Morrison he'd known him since his bum was the size of a shirt-button and he'd always talked nonsense. She didn't tell him, of course, although the image of the teacher's tiny baby bum never left her until the end of her primary school years.

She thought about her mother who worked harder than all of them although you'd never have thought it the way the men went on. Mr Morrison once gave her a project to do in school. She was about eight. She was to do a piece of in-depth research (Mr Morrison's words – English is such a clever language) so she decided to research her mother. Mr Morrison advised her to keep a diary of her mother's week so she followed her about with a clipboard that she had found, dusty, at the back of the classroom. She noted her every move and action until her mother shouted at her in frustration but then she watched her surreptitiously from behind chairs or round the corner of the croft house and that annoyed her ma even more. Nothing would deter the small researcher – not even her mother's anger. It seemed to her that her mother never stopped moving – on the few occasions she caught her sitting she was darning socks or knitting or shelling peas but even that she didn't see very often – only when she tried to creep out of bed with her clipboard.

'*Falbh air ais don leabaidh*,' her mother said smiling now at her daughter's tenacity but as the girl went back to bed she would note that her father seemed to have time in the evenings to sleep in his chair. All went into the project folder and made her father laugh his big laugh when he read it but she, for once, didn't join him in his laughter. The project had become more to her than a school exercise. She was beginning to notice things that she had never noticed before. All the time she had known her mother she had never seen her sleep.

Now, as she stood at the spring in the rain-soaked dream she thought of her young mother and of the baby due very soon. Her mother's movements were slower and heavier but still she worked as hard as ever.

And she thought about herself. Mr Morrison and her father and her mother all told her she'd be going to the High School and on to the University in Glasgow. Mr Morrison said that her future was shining and so was John's. It was exciting – the thought of them both going on and on getting cleverer and cleverer together. She couldn't imagine doing it alone but with John it would be easy.

She knew how lucky she was. Angus, her eldest brother, had a girlfriend called Eilidh who, although she was only fourteen, didn't go to school and did all the work in her house that their ma did in theirs. She cleaned and cooked and looked after the younger children because her mother had left the island. At first people pretended that she was dead but that wasn't so because she had been seen on the mainland. The adults would whisper but no one would tell the story aloud. The girl didn't care about that but she felt an instinctive sympathy for Eilidh who could not go to school because she was so busy doing other things. Boring things.

The girl bent to pick up the brimming pails and as she did she saw it come out of the rain. At first it seemed like part of her dream but it wasn't. It grew bigger and bigger. It filled and darkened further the sullen sky. A sea eagle vast and savage; attracted by the offal that her father had dumped on the beach after butchering a couple of lambs. And then came his mate, even more immense, looming out of the smirr above her and making her heart swell with elation. She could see clearly the huge yellow claws and the brilliant flash of white on the tails as they wheeled and soared over the steely loch. She watched with awe, hardly breathing. They plunged down towards the offal; claws extended, strained and then rose again. She had never seen anything so sublime. There were golden eagles aplenty in the mountains but they were not like these. These were masters of the air; these were the gods she'd read about in Greek legends. These were Icarus and Daedalus but this time conquering the elements and rejoicing. She stood for a lifetime in the soft rain, enveloped in absolute stillness and watched and watched feeling the downrush of air as they flew above her. Their magnificence compelled her like an act of worship.

Then, as if sleep-drugged, she heard the mewing of a buzzard that had joined the eagles in play. It swooped and twisted in the heavy air as if to show off its own beauty and mastery of flight but the eagles dropped the offal and turned on the buzzard in anger. It fled, heading for the mountains and a hiding place in the trees. Wherever it flew, its mighty enemies blocked its path. She watched as a beautiful but terrible dance was enacted in the sky. Now and then all three would disappear into the low clouds and her very breathing stopped until they appeared again. Eventually and inevitably the buzzard tired. Immediately, the eagle dived onto the buzzard's neck and swept it up in its claws. The other, satisfied, landed on a nearby skerrie and watched as her mate plunged the buzzard into the loch and then arched back into the sky with the struggling bird still gripped firmly in the brutal talons. Three times it did it before releasing the bird, tiny in comparison, into the water. Then he and his mate flew onto a rocky promontory, watching. The buzzard tried to swim, desperately flapping its crippled wings trying to keep afloat.

She scrambled down the hill and into the loch screaming, agonising pains in her chest and throat. She waded into the freezing water until she was up to her neck. The waves blocked her view but then she would catch a glimpse of the struggling bird still raging against death. Then it was gone. She could see it no more. She turned for the shore as the rain, heavier now, beat down on her head like lead shot and made tiny perfectly circular ripples in the loch beside her.

Climbing the hill again she reached the spring and picked up the two pails bracing and balancing her back as she had been taught. The strength of her muscles tensing comforted her. She walked back down the path to the croft, her breath still catching in her throat as a cry rose from depths that she had never known before. The rain stopped and a perfect rainbow arched above her, one end in the loch the other in the far hills. The sun came out and she could feel the hot rays on her back and her hair begin to dry as she walked home.

She thought she heard the buzzard again. The mewing much weaker now. Was this *draoidheachd* – enchantment? Were the witches still playing their eldritch tricks? She opened the gate to the yard. Angus stood there, and she realised that the mewling came from the tiny bundle in his arms. She smiled with joy and ran to look – a girl or boy? And then, from inside the cottage, she heard her father's cry of anguish.

She stopped and looked at the sky and the rain clouds now far in the distance. And she knew that, for her, it would never rain again.

Henry Bell

EDINBURGH TO GLASGOW IN EARLY DECEMBER

The trams are frozen to the tracks
so when you won't pay the fine
and they say 'get off,' you can.

The sea has swollen with ice and swallowed
Leith. But the knitting circle are keeping warm,
holed up on the second floor of the library.

The trains don't stop at Croy any more
because there's no room to let anyone on
and no one is getting off at Croy.

The subway's belching out a hot fog
that blows you back on to Queen Street
or lets you stay still if you're on the conveyor belt.

The water between the tracks is frozen
and vicars are speed-skating on the inner circle
chasing priests and dodging icicles.

By your front steps a fox
is frozen. One paw raised slightly,
its eyes looking up and its heart

stopped mid step.

Lynsey Calderwood

BAD ELEMENTS

It's raining. Invisible rain. The kind that strikes silently, like fast silver knives. I can't see it through the window of the bus, but I know it's there because the pavements are slick and black, and folk are scurrying along with hoods up and coats held tight against their throats.

I don't like travelling this early. But Mum insisted.

She's next to me, clutching a red leather purse, and from where I'm sitting it looks like she's plucked a puckered heart directly from her chest. 'All this,' she gasps, squeezing her fist tighter, 'it weighs you down.' She gives me this wide, sad-eyed look, and I turn my head away and stare out into the dark grey maw of the street. Then she sighs, a long drawn-out breath that rattles from deep within her oesophagus.

My brother, Jay, is at Mrs Pope's tonight, and Dad is 'working' in the pub. Dad's always in the pub these days, even though it's like a morgue in there. He says he can't afford to close and risk losing our remaining customers. This means Mum is always left to deal with the everyday problems that arise in our house: when I have nausea or cravings it's Mum who attends my needs; if the school calls to say Jay has been in yet another fight, it's Mum who juggles the aftermath; and if idiots from the village use our stairs as a public urinal, post bags of faeces through our letterbox or graffiti the walls of our flat with hate speech, it's Mum who single-handedly cleans up the piss and shit and poison.

We ride the bus the whole way into town then catch another one to the hospital. I don't speak for the entire journey, and she doesn't say much except to ask if I've remembered to bring a toothbrush and soap and sanitary towels. I nod and continue to stare out of the window, annoyed that she's forgotten I haven't bled for months.

I watch a fat raindrop chase a skinny raindrop and then the two merge and run down the window as one. I haven't cried either.

'You won't be allowed home the first weekend,' she says. 'But we'll be up to see you on the Saturday afternoon.'

'Right.'

'It's not an easy place to get to you,' she sighs, 'two buses and then a walk up that big hill.'

I stay quiet.

What I really want to do though is scream and hiss at her and tell her that she didn't have to come, that I could have got there myself. But I don't have the motivation for another argument. Plus, I'm not allowed to travel alone on public transport (not yet anyway), not with my 'condition'.

I don't actually care where this place is or how you get there or how long it takes. Away from school and my so-called friends, all I've got is time. A whole bloody eternity of having to live on the same planet as bigots and prats who look at me like I've got horns. Nobody asked me how I felt about going into hospital. They just dragged me up here last week under false pretences, and then ambushed me with the 'wouldn't it be nice to stay and have a rest for a little while?'

I suppose it couldn't be worse than the behavioural unit they had me in for three months before the summer holidays: all that art therapy crap, and the compulsory socialising at set times with the other day-patients when all I wanted to do was hide and sleep; plus Stupid Paul the bipolar boy kept trying to get me to kiss him. I might even have done it in the end just to shut him up, but the health-workers had me under constant surveillance.

Mum has been acting the martyr to anyone who'll listen ever since the medical team got involved. She keeps telling the same story over and over again about how traumatised she was when the police phoned that night to say they'd found me; and how I'd been left for dead beneath that underpass, smeared head to torso in my own blood.

Her talking about it makes me want to rip her larynx out. She gets offended when I say that; and says it proves just how mentally unbalanced I am; and then she uses it as further proof that they're doing the right thing by sending me away. Sometimes, I think she forgets it was me who was attacked and not her.

She also says I've become a completely different person since it happened. I think she's wrong. I still feel anger and sadness and joy and all the other normal emotions about the same things I always did. It's just that those emotions are less intense. Dr Rupert says it's because I'm clinically depressed – again, I'm not convinced he knows what he's on about either. I overheard Mum talking to him about me on the phone yesterday: she said whenever she looks at me, all she sees is this pale, hollow, imitation of her daughter; and in some ways it would have been easier if they could just have buried me.

Of course, Mum has a very black-and-white way of thinking. Like, if someone commits a crime then they must be a bad person. She says half the kids I go to school with are 'bad elements' because think drink or smoke or shoplift; or simply because I used to be friends with them but now they've turned their back on me – and maybe she's right about some of them – but she doesn't stop to think about what motivates them to do the things they do. The one thing I've never fathomed, though, is which way her moral compass would have swung if it had been someone else's daughter in my situation: would she have been giving out the tea and sympathy or the shit parcels?

Whatever Rupert's response was, it elicited a sob and a sniffle and a word of thanks, so I guess he's not a complete imbecile. Mum keeps telling me that our family is 'very, very lucky to have someone like him'. I suppose she's right because, technically, I'm not even in Rupert's jurisdiction: he took me on as a 'special project' after the headshrinker at the behavioural unit refused to keep treating me; I hated that woman with her unending questions and her finger gestures; and she insinuated that I might be better locked away in a secure unit, which is why I bit her on the wrist.

We get off the bus and walk up the hill. It takes ages and my hair is dripping because my hood won't stay up. Mum moans about how she'll have to get two buses all the way back on her own, and when I say 'why don't you get a taxi?' she just sniffs. There is a woman in front of us who is out in her nightgown and she's talking to herself and sitting in the wet grass.

Mum nudges me to walk faster, and when I turn and look over my shoulder I see that the woman has rolled forward onto her fleshy, pink belly.

There are signs everywhere that say 'No Smoking in the Hospital Grounds', but when we get closer to the Adolescent Unit I see a red car with its windows rolled down and two obese people sitting inside with lit cigarettes. Later they'll be introduced to me as Ailsa and John, the night staff.

I go through the swing door and Rupert emerges from his office at the same time.

'How are you?' he asks.

'Fine.'

He talks a lot of rubbish about the weather for a few minutes and then Mum wrings her hands and says, 'Will you be okay here?'

I shrug. 'Fine.'

'Have you got your charger for your mobile?'

'Yes.'

'And you'll phone tonight and let me know how you are?'

'Yes.'

She's acting as though it's a summer camp.

Once she goes, I am allocated a room, and an Eastern European doctor with rosy cheeks and garlic breath comes in and checks my teeth and gives me a shot of blood in a tiny plastic medicine cup.

'So,' he says, 'how long have you been a vampire?'

I sigh.

'We can help you come to terms with your condition.'

I sigh again.

'My brother was bitten in 1994 and he leads a perfectly normal life.'

'Bully for him.'

'Feeding time in one hour,' he says, and then he leaves too.

It's still raining outside.

Jim Carruth

MACINTYRE'S BIG HORSE

For Archie Stewart

When the horse died we all brought a shovel
joined Mac at the back of the paddock
to dig the grave and relive her life.

And we did so for hours, it was not a burden
for she was without doubt a great horse.
We watched again as she grew from foal

to yearling, to a mare eighteen hands high.
We recalled each field she had ploughed
the shows she won, the offspring she bore.

Completing our labours in the dark
we were glad to walk her journey again
with Mac a willing guide; we all cried.

When Mac himself died a decade later
the service was led by a visiting priest
in a rush to be somewhere else. He used

Mac's Sunday name that nobody recognised
led us in hymns that nobody knew and
in five sentences read out a stranger's life.

After the service Mac's only living relative
took time to shake hands with his lawyer.
They filled in his grave with a JCB.

Linda Cracknell

THE OTHER SIDE OF STONE

Some days it's just the wee fellow who watches me. I see him through the hazel-arch of the workshop when I turn my head, and he's there when I take my tools out to the forge to be licked sharp in the flames. He perches on the top of the rubble pile, or on a post, and observes. A smart-looker he is, with his white collar and chestnut stomach. Out of his dark face comes a scolding cry when there's someone coming. He's an unquiet bird then, with his 'clack-clack-clack,' for all as if he's bashing two stones together.

If the women hear him they turn their backs, pull their caps over their cheeks like blinkers, wondering who the *rosad* will fall upon.

'Will it be your father who wakes up blind?' I tease them as they go by. 'Or your man that falls from a crag and loses the use of his legs? Or maybe the leg in-between will drop off!'

It's not for a man of my age to be feared of a bird the size of my thumb. And the fellow's my friend is he not? He's my steady companion, watching me force the chisel upon this rock that's so brute-hard my scours and drafts will be there to see for centuries to come.

Other days it seems I've the whole village gathered about me – the Camerons and Macgregors and Menzies and Macfarlanes. There's this rare excitement lighting up the place, the blether and rumours dashing between cottages. Folk flock about here, any time of day or night, quite bespelled by the thing clambering towards the heavens in steel and wood and stone.

They whisper about the man on the horse, come from the south to build a new mountain in their midst, bringing wool-spinners under the one pitched roof to make them all rich. Of course we've heard of whole forests of machinery-mills going up in the south, but to have such a thing here all on its own has them quite puffed up. The glamour of it's rosied their cheeks and has them bobbing and smiling when the man comes by to see progress. An awe-struck hush comes upon them save for those who've a few words of the English.

He has a quiet way about him, and a good smile, and they say he speaks of new markets and the 'fancy' trade for trousers, and protective checks for the estates. The minister tells me the man wishes to stop a trade as well as to start one. He has important business as far away as London, where he must join with other grand men to bring freedom to African people sold as slaves.

As they've got used to me, the men have started to bring their whisky and stories into the workshop. At first they stayed on their feet, but these days they squat on a piece of rubble they've each brought in from the pile. And I keep on with my work on the dressings, easing my stiff legs as I stretch to reach the whole length of the slab, taming it into smooth lines as it's to be the dedication stone above the door, and hold the whole thing up.

On the inside of my head I speak with the stone, listen to its testimony, while the men's stories chip away on the outside. I keep at it till the gloaming or the whisky steal the features from its face. Or when the rattles and gurgles in my lungs pull me down, and I wrench the cloth from my mouth, and join the men.

As I shake the white-finger from my hand, they put their questions upon me about where I've come from, and how it was to work on the grand tower all those years at Taymouth, the castle they still call 'Slippery John's'. Pinned in an ice-scoured valley it was, I say, with a rocky ridge on each side. We were building up through four floors to try and get out of the shade in winter. But the topping-out, well that was a fair day, so it was.

Then they ask me about my road here. 'Which one did you take, journeyman?' they want to know. And I know why they ask. I've heard of folk who'll go the long way around to avoid the ford at Loch an Daimh and the fear of having the flesh torn from them. Even myself, I took care to get over it before nightfall, with my slow shuffle from the far valley jarred and halted all the way by the cough. Surely it'll be my last journey to find work, surely my last.

They tell me about this weaver they knew, coming that way, over the shoulder of the hill in daylight, and how he called at a nearby cottage for directions. He met a man there, tall and lean, a schoolmaster so he said, all alone. The weaver was persuaded to stay awhile for a drink and so was belated.

As the weaver crossed the ford between loch and cliff just after the gloaming, he heard feet coming towards him on the polished track, cloven feet, and found himself faced by a goat on its hind legs with cat's claws for hands, dog's fangs and a human face. But this weaver had a special weapon. To the schoolmaster he'd called it his 'cat behind the hip' – the *sgian dubh* was what he meant – and this goat-demon wasn't expecting the blade he took in his chest, went roaring off into the night with a great frothing and gurgling of blood in his throat.

The travelling weaver ran back to the schoolmaster's cottage for help, and what did he find? Nothing but the schoolmaster lying in bed and his life leaving him from a wound in his chest. The weaver hurried on down here to the village and gave the bell-man something to shout the next morning.

'The cat behind the hip': it's a fine way of calling it.

'We should put that story on young Archie there,' one of the old boys cackles, for not one of them can recall, now, exactly who this weaver was. The story needs a new subject. He points over at the lad with the raven hair and shock-blue eyes. We're all sitting in gloom, warmed with the lantern and mixing whisky-mist breath, and I see the lad's hands twisting a dance with each other but also his wee grim smile. He comes in with the men these days, since his da's away with the fever.

'He's needing a turn as hero, is he not?' The old boy cackles on. 'Then the lassies'll flock to him like the starlings at even.'

I leave my own work at intervals during the day, when my back's stabbed with the needles from leaning too long over the banker. I take a stroll around the other masons at their work. They've stones just a small size compared to mine, coloured dark or sand or even pale blue. They're levelling them so they'll sit one over the other right up into the sky. You have to understand the pull of the earth to get that right. Masons are like God in that way I always think. I take a look at each, weigh it with my ancient eye, give the man my nod or word.

But there's one I stare at while he works, and when he steps back, I cough up a great gobbet of spittle and aim it at the top face of his rock. The wet brings out those tiny flecks of red that sometimes worm in this strange, hard stone.

Mason to mason, this young man steels his accusing eyes into mine, still a midgie on a mountain in his understanding. His lips are pushed into a purse of indignation. The gobbet slicks towards the ground making a long, stained line of charcoal. He's to learn respect, to know that each day for the rock is measured in a man's million years.

'That bed's not straight,' I say, pointing at the top side, and walk away with the chick's eyes burrowing into my back, as he digests his lesson.

I go back to my own slab, its long straight grey back made perfectly flat, the beds and joints already prepared to fit the place of pride above the door. I'm ready to start the face now, and the four bearded fixers come, levering it over to expose the last untreated surface. I take up the boaster.

Later, the wee fellow clacks his warning outside, and there's young Archie, putting his blue eyes on me, and his hand on the rock. It's a soft hand yet, without my knobbled joints and skin cracked to weeping with the cold and heat and the rough care of the stone. He wants to learn, he says, and so he starts to come each day to watch between his chores, just like the wee fellow perched outside.

He gets used to speaking, when his elders aren't about, and he tells me of a lass on their farm, her dress the colour of new birch leaves, and her hair bright yellow like the whins aflame. Tall and thin, he says, and she watches the cows without being asked to. His mother pours milk into the hollow of a rock at the gateway each evening, and by the morning it's supped quite clean away.

'And you've seen her,' I say. 'Have you spoken?'

But he's only glanced her from the corner of his eye, he says, as she goes between the cows and the loch. I nod, and recognise in myself the first fret gnawing.

He comes out with me to the forge and I show him how to heat the chisels till they're rowanberry-red, then douse the steel in water for its angry display of spit and steam, to see the colour of the temper. 'See,' I say. 'When it's cooled – as blue as a raven's wing – it's fit for anything.'

He says he'll remember that.

'And you've to be careful with the lassies, you'll remember that fine too?' I warn him.

Next time the horse-mannie comes, his son rides next to him, barely older than Archie I suppose, but acting like a man of business. I shake my head at the father, in place of words of the English, at the picture he brings of his family monogram for the dedication stone. I sweep my fingers around its curves and intricacies. It'll be a carver he wants, not a master-mason, to give him that. I show him by tapping a point with the mallet, how easily it slips off the cruel hardness of this local stone. I could manage to carve the pen of course, but what we do not share the words for, I cannot say to him – why would anyone wish a crow to decorate their building? He hangs his head, stops his smiling for a minute, nodding bitterly at his son.

But the next day back they come with a new idea, a simpler one. The year. That's all that's needed for a dedication stone. The smile flicks across his face like sun on the hill on a wild March day, and the son laughs and laughs when he sees that I agree. The father even draws it for me on a piece of wood, as if I can't carry the shape in my own head. I like to keep designs in there so the carving appears as a miracle of sorts, folk gathering to see, ducking the shards flying from the chisel in case they should seek out cheek or eye. But that's when I'm working with slate, the luxury of butter, not this cruel stone.

'Better you'd built it in 1741 or 1477,' I find a way to say by showing him the ease of making straight lines on a length of timber. But 1831 has been chosen with all its double curves, and this stone has been chosen, hacked from the earth and dragged here by oxen as quarry block. A fine stone since they're thinking to plant something permanent and wise here. I see how the land's been captured from marsh, the water sucked from it and gathered with that fall of the river to make a fast channel to drive the wheel.

Each day villagers' necks crane back further to see the top as the stone gathers upwards to dwarf the church and build a spectacle. The shadow we cast grows daily, stretching out across the grass, towards the inn and the row of cottages. It's got the mouth of the Campbell woman flickering up and down like the wee bird's tail, as she stands in her doorway knee-deep in children, half agleed, half afraid, now the sun has been blocked from her cottage.

Young Archie comes back, hand on the stone and an eye on me, like he's trying to draw wisdom from us both. He's telling me how his mother's become firm, saying now her man is cold she's not able to spare milk for a good-for-nothing lass. The rock under my hand tells me he will speak of missing calves or dead babies. But he just says how he misses seeing the lass.

'Would you not be better to give your eye to the young Macgregor girl with her long hair, or the one who has a strawberry for a mouth, and hair to match?' I say. For the other, I think, will rove, choosing to cause harm or not as the fancy takes her.

I nod away his hand, pull the cloth back over my mouth, and give the chisel to the stone.

The younger horse-mannie comes back again and takes us by surprise in the workshop, so that The Smuggler has to hurry out with a keg bulged under his coat and his cheeks still swollen with a gobful. The father is in London stopping one business whilst the building of another is entrusted to his son. I show him with my hand how I've smoothed the face with the boaster, and how it's ready now for carving. We both stare at it. It's a rock that has different things to reveal – its glint or its darkness under certain lights or drenches. He comes close and lays his face against it. It's like he's kissing it or whispering a secret.

It puts me in mind of that story the men tell of the reiver come from the north who on his way falls for a lassie minding a favourite cow. When she asked for the third time where he came from and what his business was, he could not hold out and so instead of telling her, he unburdened himself by whispering it to the cow. 'Black cow, come midnight, you'll be half the way to Lochaber,' he said. He wasn't to know the lassie was the Laird's daughter, her ears sharp, and so

the cottage-folk were armed and ready for the raid. It was a black
night all right for Lochaber.

Whisper to a cow if you will, but whispering to a rock will do less
than a dog-rose petal touching the crag up there as it floats down-
wards, swinging this way and then that like a wee boat caught in the
wind. Isn't the hardest strike I can make with my bolster as weak to
this rock as a single kiss? But then the young mannie feels in his
pocket and brings out a swatch of woollen fabric, puts it against the
stone, and sure enough if you squint your eye, it's of a colour with
it, in tiny checks of grey, black and brown. We catch eyes and out of
him tumbles his laugh that sparks up my own.

Archie comes back speaking of a calf pushed away by its mother.
They gave it the amulet but there's some stronger magic at work, for
she still rejected it. So the calf has folded its legs under itself, and is
weak-lidded about the eyes. A frown has drawn itself across Archie's
brow as he watches me turn the curves of the '3' with the point.

When I look aside to Archie's eyes, I see the whins still blazing in
their reflection. She still plays her mischief.

The next day he comes, and the calf has died. The family are
saddened without new life about them and have lost the promise of
a sale. He looks to the building, and asks when it will be finished,
when will there be work?

Worse news comes. There's a wee brother, Robbie, that sometimes
trails after Archie, a match for him in raven and blue. He likes to
play on the floor, building and balancing stones or chippings, one
above the other, or enjoying the weight of my tools and laying them
out in a long line. Robbie is now roaring with a fever. Archie's face
takes on the frowns and wrinkles of ancient rock.

'Would your mother not think of putting out the milk again?'
I ask him.

But the cow has dried up.

He goes away round-shouldered and slow while my lungs rattle
and erupt, stealing speech.

I look at the patient rock that waits with its face up, the year I've
marked upon it like a flea-bite in its story. I dust off the surface, and
see that it is fine, that the light will catch it almost as from a plate

of silver. And on the top bed, where it will be hidden, I make my mark: a straight line topped with a pointing triangle, and two more hanging from one side. It will breathe secretly in the joint against the stone above.

Then I think of the lad, so young to be so troubled, and the lass, the *glaistig*, displaced and vengeful. It brings a cold cloak-mist about my shoulders.

The four beards come at my summons and roll the stone over, lifting with bent, trembling legs. The back of the stone now faces upwards on the banker. I nod them away to be alone with it. My guard, the wee fellow with the white collar chapping on his pile of rubble, is the only one who sees what I do. The plan of it is already carved in my mind. The long lines of an A-shaped dress on a figure tall and thin. Her face straight-edged, hair a series of small chips spiking from her head like a halo of flames. A chip kissed into the stone for each eye, and for a nose.

Then the beards are carrying the stone to its place, sliding it up the prepared planks, too hard-muscled and lung-blown to notice my extra design. She is turned to face inwards, hidden against iron and timber whilst the proud date-inscribed face meets the world, like a bell-man proclaiming a revolution. A scattered cheer goes up and a keg is passed low between the men who've paused in their work.

I begin to gather my tools into the bag, checking they are all there by number and all carry my mark. When I leave the workshop I sense an absence. There's no sign of my smart-looking friend, the bird. Perhaps he will clack his stones and make his new guard atop the growing grey walls.

I look west towards the loch that will power this place, and towards the lad's farm. I suck on a hope that his family will be free of the *glaistig* now that I've given her a place to stay. And then a cough takes me and bends me double, and it's a few moments before I can straighten up again, ready to be on my way.

Anna Crowe

POEM

After Banks's Oar-Fish, **Regalecus banksii**

Impelled to the surface
by who knows
what grim upheaval
down there in the dark,
she swims to us
through a tangle
of fishermen's tales
to cast herself ashore
on the quiet coasts
of remote islands.
Few folk ever see her,
yet her monstrous length
is the clattered talk
of the ocean-going albatross,
the mournful complaint
of the great northern loon,
the grey seal's moan.
We can only dream
of her skin of smooth silver,
her long, long back
pricked out with fins
like crimson flames.
For now, all we have
is this painted cast
of her small neat head,
her shining, sightless eyes.

Sylvia Dow

SHE SAID: HE SAID: I SAID

Well, she said. I'm not blaming you, she said. I'm not blaming anybody.
No. Really. Really I'm not.

Because bottom line is it was going to happen anyway. Wasn't it?

Don't answer that. I can see it on your face. Written all over your face. You agree with me don't you? No. No. No words.

I know you're with me on this.

But, she said, although I don't blame you entirely, she said, you've got to admit you did play a part in this. A major part.

It was not, I repeat not, all down to him.

O I admit he's a bit, how can I put it, weak. Yes weak – no moral backbone.

This isn't the first time it's happened. Were you aware of that?

He feels sorry for people. Wants to help out. Especially where someone is, what's the right word, needy.

And you were needy, weren't you, girl? You. Were. Needy.

She said.

I said. Yes.

Needy, yes. And he took pity on you.

He never seems to figure out that young pretty girls have wiles.

My mother used to warn me about wiles.

Young women's wiles.

Abjure the pleasures of the flesh that's what she used to tell me. Except where necessary.

She had many important rules for marriage.

Clothes, for example. Dress demurely. And when you go to bed at night don't leave your underwear on show, don't leave it on a chair for example. Put it away in a drawer. It's not fitting he should see your underwear.

Did you tuck away your underwear? Did you? I can see by your face you didn't, she said.

There's a time and a place for marital relations. And a reason. Procreation.

Didn't quite go that way for us of course, so with that reason no longer an issue, the bed thing stopped being an issue too.

Thankfully.

I can see you're in pain, she said.

I do tie a very good knot she said. Thanks to the Girl Guides.

A moral pathway for girls. Were you a Girl Guide? Were you? She said.

I said. No.

No. Thought not.

And what will I do with you now Miss no morals?

Miss short skirt. Miss showing her undies to all and sundry. Miss Jezebel.

What should I do to punish you for taking advantage of a poor weak man? What, eh?

Keep your mouth shut. I'm the one who will decide.

When I was young, she said, I dreamt of Mr Right. A good clean man, a good clean house, good clean babies. And I almost got all of these.

But not quite, she said. Not quite.

Did you dream of that too?

And look at where your failure to achieve that has brought you. Look where lust has led you. She said.

There are things I could do to make you suffer.

What do you say to that eh?

Tell me your thoughts pretty little girl, she said. Tell me your thoughts.

I said. Nothing.

Silence. Darkness. Silence.

I said nothing the first time. When he asked me.

It's not that I'm shy. I sometimes come over as shy. Reserved.

I don't like to give too much away. It's safer. I've always thought that.

But he was. Attractive, yes, very attractive.

Not flash, or in your face, or pushy. That was good.

Older, quite a bit older than me of course. That was attractive too.

When he asked me, I couldn't help smiling, just a little.

He smiled too, a shining through his eyes kind of smile.

An admiring kind of smile. Not sleazy. Honest admiration.

I knew of course. About her. His wife. No. That's wrong. I didn't know *about* her. Just that she existed. That he had a wife.

I didn't care.

That may be surprising. I'm surprised myself. But I didn't care. At all actually.

I cared about him. About his admiration. I felt his need.

I had needs too. So when he asked me.

When he said what he said.

I said. Yes.

Darkness. Quiet. Car passing.

She said nothing at first. When I asked her. She seemed shy, very, yes, reserved. But lovely, really lovely. Not flaunting her wares kind of thing.

Reserved.

Sitting there, face lit up by the computer screen, little sliver of a semi-smile.

Then she said. Very quietly. Yes.

And she looked straight at me.

Were her eyes green? Yes I believe they were. Are. Green, flecked with amber.

She looked straight at me but not in a bold way, you understand. With honesty, I think that's the correct phrase. Or perhaps with openness.

Later on of course I uncovered her other side. Not a wild side exactly. More of a secret side.

Some of her secrets:

She smoked black Russian cigarettes. I loved the sexual smell of them. The taste of them when I kissed her.

When we kissed. It was a mutual thing.

She had ambition. To better herself. She saw a future that did not include being an administrator in our or anyone's office. I knew I could help her with that. I wanted to help her with that.

She was interested in everything. Politics, soap operas, foreign countries, celebrity gossip, wide musical tastes. You could not define her by her interests.

She was without vanity. I never saw her look in a mirror. Or worry about her appearance. A kind of inner confidence maybe?

Two of her toes are webbed. Left foot, toes three and four. Fascinating.

Fascinating, yes, right from the outset she was utterly fascinating.

She had secrets and she could keep a secret. At least our secret.

No guilt. I don't know what her feelings were on the subject, but I had no guilt.

Perhaps I've had plenty of practice. You could say that with some justice.

Perhaps I should have. Felt guilt. She was so much younger. Years younger.

Perhaps that's why one day she just wasn't there any more. Not at the office. Not at her flat. Not answering her phone.

Perhaps she just felt it was time, you know, time to draw a line, make an end, move on.

Perhaps.

But I do miss her. Quite a bit, truth be told.

Life goes on, however. That's always been my motto. It's one that has served me well.

Someone in the office asked if I had seen her recently.

I said. No.

No.

Silence. Moonlight.

She said. I've brought you something to eat. Something healthy.

Can't have you pegging out on me, she said, can I?

All captives have to be fed.

It's the law isn't it? And if it isn't it should be. At the very least it's my moral duty.

Not that you'd know much about morals, she said.

Not having any yourself.

And speaking of morals.

When I met him, when he and I got together, it was all done, how should I put it, properly. Yes. With proper regard to what's appropriate, what's acceptable. What's right.

It was in his office, she said, that we met. Of course he wasn't the manager then.

He wasn't my boss. He was never my boss.

He smiled at me whenever he passed my desk.

The kind of smile that shone through his eyes.

The kind of smile that meant sincere admiration.

I lived for that smile she said. Waited for it every day.

You'll know all about that I expect.

After a while I'd smile back. I could tell he liked that. That he liked me.

And when he asked me I said.

I said.

It was all done with complete propriety of course, I made sure of that.

The only correct or possible outcome was marriage.

But all that was a long time ago. How many years? I've lost count.

I've lost a lot of things.

Too many things.

Of course my mother didn't like him. Not trustworthy was her verdict.

A bit of a lad. A wandering eye. A way with the ladies. Trouble.

And you and I, girl, we know that to be true. Don't we? she said. Don't we?

I said. Yes.

Look, I said. Listen.

I'm sorry, I said.

I never meant to harm you.

To be honest I said I never thought about you. Never gave you a moment's thought.

I regret that now of course. I will always regret that.

I can see you're hurting, I said. I can see that he's not the man I thought he was.

Or maybe he was and I liked that he was, but now I don't.

If you see what I mean, I said.

Sorry, I said. Sorry.

I'm hurting too. In every sense of the word.

You must see that.

Everyone makes mistakes I said. You must have made mistakes. Haven't you?

She said. I'll have to have a little think about that.

Silence. Darkness, Daylight.

Daylight. And she's silhouetted in the door with light behind her shoulders and she has something in her hand and my eyes are straining against the light but I can see what she's holding is large and chunky and she's holding it up aggressively and my hands are tied. I. Can't. Move. My. Hands.

And I'm afraid. Paralysed with fear.

I'm remembering once when I was having minor surgery I woke momentarily from the anaesthetic, they tell you it can't happen but it does, and the pain is severe, but the worst thing is the paralysis. You can't move. At all.

Paralysis.

Suddenly there's a demon of a driving force surging from my toes to the top of my head, and I struggle to my feet and launch myself at her, she opening her mouth to speak, me on a forward trajectory, on a mission to get free to get out of there to the daylight. Out of the dark. Into the light. Out.

I ram my head into her.

She topples over.

There's a cracking noise.

She's hit her head on the path. She's bleeding.

A strange *cruk cruk* noise is coming from her chest.

Still clasped in her hand is my bag, my backpack.

No. No. No. No. No.

Sunshine. Birds. Time suspended.

Are you all right? I said. Are you?

She said.

She said.

Nothing.

Louise Farquhar

MUM AND I

It's only Mum and I; Dad is dead. Well, sort of. Mum and Auntie Judith always told me he was dead. Recently I started to think he wasn't so I brought it up with Mum while we ate lunch in the kitchen. She kept staring at her sandwich while I asked her questions. *Did she have photos of him? Where were his things? Where was he buried?* Her mouth tightened around the edges while I was speaking. Turns out he left when I was born.

I don't know him so I don't miss him. It's been fine, just the two of us, Mum and I.

In the mornings before school, at the jam-packed café near our flat, I get to choose what I want for breakfast. Square sausage, streaky bacon cooked extra crispy, potato scone and a fried egg. Mum only has tea. I like it there, except for the men. They swagger over like cowboys, resting an arm on the table while they lean in with smelly coffee breath. She smiles when they tell her she's beautiful. They're the same in the street, on the way to the train, calling out from vans and whistling loudly making everyone stare. Sometimes it even happens at the station. I think it's her black uniform (she works at the Savannah Beauty Salon on Crow Road) or maybe her lovely long hair. Most of the time she just laughs, but sometimes she listens. I don't speak to them, turning the other way so they can't catch my eye. Even if they ruffle my hair I don't look. Once a man asked if I had a boyfriend. *I'm only nine*, I snapped. He winked which made me hate him more.

Sometimes one appears at the front door. Before they arrive I know they're coming. Mum goes into the bathroom for a long time. When she comes out the walls are damp from the hot bath and the air is thick with the scent of soap and perfume. I write my name on the mirror. She hangs different dresses on the front of her wardrobe and scatters tights, necklaces and underwear on the bed. I don't help choose her outfit; I want her to stay in with me and watch TV.

She tells me to lock the door when they go out. She won't be late. This is my special time. I take a can of Irn Bru from the fridge and sweeties from the cupboard. I'm allowed to choose as many movies as I want (as long as they're PG) and watch them until I fall asleep on the sofa. I don't hear her come home.

One of the men was a travel agent so we got a free night in a hotel, the two of us. Another gave her a job in his restaurant and she brought home pizza every night. The best was the lawyer. He was fat and grey but there was always lots of money when he was around. He was flash. He even promised me a pony. I told Bethany at school about him but I soon wished I hadn't, when he stopped visiting.

Mum cried for a while after that man. She said we were broke. She said we might need to go back to Gran's house. I don't know why she would want to go there. Gran has a wrinkly, pointy face with black eyes, like the dead shrivelled mouse I found in the back court. Her head is covered in tight, purplish-grey rolls of hair and she *tuts* instead of talks. All the rooms in her house are cold. We lived there for a while when I was little. Gran never stops cleaning. When Mum smoked a cigarette Gran flung open every window in the house and coughed. They argued a lot, in whispered voices, while I played with a jewellery box in the bedroom, opening and closing the lid to catch out the music. At night Mum would snuggle in with me and tell stories about far away places with white sandy beaches, palm trees and rainbow-coloured fish. We're best friends forever – BFF.

A few weeks ago a new man came to the flat. He's called Paul. He's visited a few times since then. I don't usually think about their names but Paul is different. I can't find much really wrong with him; I quite like him. There's nothing showy about Paul and he speaks quietly and says *no problem* a lot to Mum. He tilts his head when he looks at her and smiles. He never winks at me or ruffles my hair. Mum's cheeks went all red the first time he came to the door. His clothes don't bother me either. I hate the tight jeans some of the other men wear, and I don't like beards. They're the worst. Paul doesn't have a beard, or a moustache. He wears those Gap chino trousers, clean and ironed, with a shirt and no tie. His shoes are brown lace-ups with no scuffs. It always looks silly when grown-up men wear trainers. I'm glad he doesn't. The other night, when he was leaving, I peeked through a crack in the bedroom door and watched them kissing. His hands stayed still on Mum's waist, which was good. Some of the other men's hands fidget all over her body and even touch her boobs – which is disgusting. When they were finished he said *I'm the luckiest man in the world to have you*. Mum held his face for a moment but didn't speak. I think she was crying.

She says he's divorced and works as an engineer for the electricity company. I was disappointed when I heard this because I don't think he can afford a pony. He does bring presents though: chocolates and flowers for Mum and a Nintendo game for me. He knows I like *The Sims* because I played it on his phone once when they were talking and I was bored. Paul likes the cinema, which is really cool. We all went last night, to the Odeon in town. He bought popcorn AND ice cream AND pick-and-mix AND juice. I never get all those things when I go with Mum. After, he came back to the flat with us and they started drinking wine so I went to bed.

This morning Paul was still at home. That hasn't happened before, with the other men. I bumped into him coming out of the bathroom. I stood in the hall in my Honey Monster pyjamas and he stood in the doorway with a fluffy pink towel round his waist and nothing else. Weird. Everything was totally silent for a minute; then he asked if I liked his outfit. It was funny. I shrugged and he laughed. Mum appeared from the bedroom, dressed, thankfully, and said we were all going to the café for breakfast. Her skin looked all peachy and she kept giggling. My mum's so beautiful.

In the café, the table I like best is too small for three people so we took the bigger one in the corner. Mum huddled up on the bench beside Paul. He ordered two bacon rolls and coffee for him, a hot chocolate for me as well as my fry-up and toast for Mum to go with her tea. They held hands under the table while we waited for our food. As we ate breakfast he told us all about the electricity pylons and how he climbs them sometimes when they need fixed. *They buzz really loudly*, he said. When he went to the toilet Mum rummaged in her handbag for her favourite coral lipstick and put some on. As she held up a shiny spoon to her face, checking her reflection, a man started to come towards the table. I remembered him; he was the one with the silver BMW and the bad temper. I didn't want him near Mum, or Paul. I stuck my tongue out at him. Mum didn't see. She would have flipped because one of her rules is to be polite. He stopped dead. Paul appeared and budged my mum along the bench so he could sit down. My eyes darted towards the BMW man. *Go away! Go Away!* I thought. He turned and left without bothering her. Then it was just the three of us, and I liked that.

Graham Fulton

WHATEVER YOU DO DON'T SMILE

looking subnormal in a photo booth
only takes a neutron of the consciousness
it took
in the old days
when you had to wait a week
for 4 sloppy photos
to slide out of the slot
in a strangely sexual way
on the side of a weird machine
with a wee overworked man inside
frantically developing at the speed of light,
while now
you twirl the chair to the demanded height
and listen to the female robot instructions
and place your digital head
precisely
within the red oval
and *whatever you do don't smile*
whatever you do don't smile,
until it's all done
and you get your pictures 51 seconds later
and stare at them in disbelief
and do it all again
in the hope that this time
Brad Pitt's or The Elephant Man's
or anyone else's face will be there
instead of your own

Gordon Gibson

SIRLOIN

When Thomas and his mother go to the supermarket on Saturday mornings, they always buy the same things. He doesn't get upset when she refuses to put something in the trolley that catches his eye, though it doesn't stop him asking. Sweets he has seen advertised on television perhaps, or a new breakfast cereal being promoted in the store. But by now he knows that her answer will be 'No chance'.

'You must think I'm made of money. It takes me all my time to buy enough to feed you.' Then she will give her special smile and add 'Hollow-legs'.

Thomas is ten – old enough to understand by now that money is always short, despite the long hours she works as a cleaner. And he knows she tries her best to make sure he always has enough to eat.

It's just that, when they sit together on the couch watching some fancy chef on TV, he can't help saying, 'That looks great, Mum. I wish we could try it.'

And she makes a noise in her throat that doesn't mean either yes or no, but sounds a little bit sad, and he wishes he hadn't said anything at all.

But today, though it started normally enough, things have gone seriously wrong. They've walked into town, and he's told her about all that happened at school yesterday. She always asks him lots of questions and jokes with him about the other pupils, and the pretty young teacher that he likes so much. He knows he's lucky that he gets on well with his mum. Not like some other boys at school who never stop complaining how their mothers boss them about. His mum is definitely in charge, but she's never unreasonable. She calls him 'pal', and that's how it feels.

They have a well-practised routine for the supermarket. His mum makes a list that is much the same every week and, in the store, she inspects the meat, vegetables and fruit, choosing best value. While she does this, she sends him off to bring back tins or packets from the shelves. He knows where to find things, and he runs back to place them in the trolley then sets off to fetch another item.

He knows he will always remember the moment when today went wrong: he is bringing back a packet of economy dried spaghetti. His mum is leaning over a display of meat, all neatly packed in white polystyrene trays with plastic wrapping. She is searching through the packets, and he decides to creep up quietly behind her and give her a surprise. It will make her jump, and then giggle.

He approaches from the far end of the aisle, moving slowly through the other shoppers, watching in case she turns round and sees him. She picks up a flat pack of meat, about the size of a library book, but, as she is about to place it in the trolley, she drops it, and goes down on one knee to pick it up again. When she stands up, there is no packet of meat to be seen.

Thomas feels his heart beating quickly and strongly. It's a strange feeling, like being afraid without knowing what there is to fear. Something is not right. He stops, watching from a distance. He forgets about giving her a surprise. What's happening? What has become of the packet?

She turns around, looking in all directions, and her eyes fall upon him. She remains still, one hand on the shopping trolley, facing towards him. He somehow expects her to be annoyed with him, but she wears an expression as if she is sorry about something, the way she looks when she's tired or pleading with him to behave.

She calls to him, 'Come on, slowcoach,' and, turning back towards the trolley, continues down the aisle. He catches up with her, and walks beside her, wanting to ask what she has been doing, afraid in case what he suspects is true. He looks in the trolley for the poly-styrene packet, but it isn't amongst the shopping.

His mum's anorak is unzipped, and hanging open. She is wearing a long woolly sweater that stretches down past her waist. Her blue jeans are tight, and he can see the bulge of her purse in the side pocket. He moves closer to her and slips his arm around her, leaning towards her so that he bumps against the anorak. Through the padded nylon he feels something rectangular in an inside pocket.

They go on shopping, just like every other Saturday, except that his heart continues to thump inside his chest, and he feels his arms and hands trembling. He watches his mother's every movement, hoping she is going to reach into the hidden inside pocket, draw out the packet of meat and place it on top of the other groceries. When she sends him to fetch a tin of beans from a shelf, he races back and looks into the trolley to see if the meat is there, but it has not appeared. Again and again he stares up into her face, searching for – he doesn't know what – some signal of explanation.

But she does not return his gaze. She does not look towards him. She busies herself making her choices from the cabinets, or staring intently at the shopping list she holds in her left hand. When she tells him which goods he is to collect next, she does so without looking in his direction. By the time they reach the checkout, he knows that the packet of meat is not going to appear in the trolley.

His mother is friendly with the girl who operates the till, and, as usual, chats away to her brightly while lifting her purchases from the trolley onto the rubber conveyor belt. Then, when they have been scanned, she packs them into plastic bags. Finally, she takes out her purse from the side pocket of her jeans, and carefully counts out the exact amount of money that is showing on the electronic display. Everything looks completely normal, but Thomas feels sick. He's sure that something terrible is about to happen.

*

But nothing happens. They hardly talk on the way home. His mother seems weary as she trudges along, a plastic bag of shopping in each hand, her shoulders stooped. Usually he nags until she allows him to carry a bag, but not today.

Back at the flat, she goes into the kitchen and stacks the shopping on the table. He leans against the door frame, watching her. She hasn't taken off her anorak yet, and he notices how she turns her back to him before she lets it slip from her shoulders. Her movements are awkward. When she leaves the kitchen, to hang the anorak in the hall cupboard, he sees that the packet of meat is lying on the table with the rest of the shopping.

*

Sometimes there is a treat for dinner if there has been a special offer at the supermarket, or one of her clients has given her a tip. Something unusual – chicken drumsticks are his favourite, or lamb curry with white fluffy rice. When this happens, she always makes a fuss in advance, saying that there will be something great to eat, but refusing to tell him what it will be. She makes him stay in the living room, asking him to try to guess what is making the delicious cooking smell that is drifting through from the kitchen.

Tonight, although the smell from the kitchen makes his mouth water, she says nothing about the meal. He lies on the couch in the living room, staring at the television without taking anything in, until she calls for him to come and wash his hands. When he goes through, the kitchen table is set and she is lifting food from the cooker onto their plates.

'What is it?' he asks. His back is turned to her as he soaps his hands.

'Sirloin steak and onions. And chips too,' she says.

'I don't want any sirloin steak,' Thomas says. 'I don't like it.'

'How do you know you don't like it?' she says. 'I don't think you've ever tasted it.'

He sits at the table, but is unable to eat. With his mother's eyes on him, he cuts a tiny piece of the meat, and puts it into his mouth. He has made up his mind: he will not eat; he will spit the meat back onto his plate.

But it tastes wonderful. It is so delicious that, before he can stop himself, he has chewed and swallowed it. With tears forming in the corners of his eyes, he cannot stop himself from devouring the rest of the steak. He is horrified by the pleasure that the unfamiliar taste gives.

His mother smiles at him across the table. It is her special smile.

'I thought you'd like it,' she says. 'Something a bit different.'

Mandy Haggith

ALPHABET

After Inger Christensen

Affirmation
Ash trees are therefore life is.

Beginning
Birches, bracken, brambles and birds,
a bourach, a beautiful bourach.

Continuation
At the coast, a rock-sea confusion.
Crows cruise, caw, congregate on a corpse.
Corrupting carbohydrates become compost.

Death
Dandelions are, dunnochs are, Dad is.
I feel down. I don't do. I doubt.
Duties are doubled.
But dandelions are, and daffodils definitely are too.

Elegy
Evening comes.
Everything exists.
Everything nothing.
Everything exists.
Evening comes.

Fire
I find fire,
flames, fog, finches, frogs and friends.
Looking at the future,
fear, fruit, fiction and freedom

flourish,
fortunes do not.

Grave
good
grey
ground
silence
good
grey
ground

Happiness
You would want us not to grieve too long
so I go to the old hazel tree and lie down
here and now where you are no longer.
You taught me never to hate anyone
no matter how horrible they seem.
We have choices, all life long, until the end.
My hormones are changing, hot flushes happen.
The hazel catkins open tiny yellow flowers.

Imagination
An ivory carving
conjures the iron age
into the present.
Indigo sky:
instant tempest.
Inside others
intractable secrets.
The inner workings of a mind
make the impossible possible.

Justice
Better than a joke
seeing a wrong righted.
Take money from the rich
give it to the poor.
Is it so difficult?
Just listen.
Stop and help.
Gang up together
against the powerful, for good.
Jam tomorrow.

Killing
Does the kingfisher
give itself up to the hawk?
Is kelp
thrown up onto the beach,
clinging with its holdfast to a stone,
murdered by the sea?
Is my omelette
haunted
by unborn feathers and clucking?
Frosted frogspawn on the pond.
Bones along the shore.

Lots
Lots of letters.
Lots of lilies and daffodils.
Lots of leaves.
Lots of liverworts and mosses.
Lots of lovely lichens.
Lots of little animals: woodlice, earwigs, beetles.

Lots of lions: cats, statues and flags.
Lots of lying around.
Lots of lying for your life.
Lots of life.
Lots of loose ends.
Lots of love.

Mum
mourning
my
mother
means
missing
maternal
messages

months
minus
mum
memories
must
make-do

Now
The day he had to leave
I sat with my brother by Mum's bedside, crying.
'Go back to your little family,' she said,
'they need you.'

We talked about the nursery trees
in the Pacific Rainforest, where he lives,
great cedars that live a thousand years,

stand dead five hundred more
then fall, to feed another generation.

They give their nitrogen, nutrients, nature.
Even as only a long, low mound in the woods
the mother tree gives everything
to nourish her offspring.

Only
As there is no omniscient being,
no omnipotent force,
we must be optimistic
as we go from our origins
to oblivion,
from the open-mouthed yowl
to our obituary,
on the way, enjoying
owls in osiers
ogres on oboes
onomatopoeia
occasional orneriness or obduracy
and, obviously, oranges, often.

Primroses
Primroses form patches in woods.
Primrose leaves poke through leaf litter.
Primroses photosynthesise.
Primroses are peaceful.
Primrose petals are so delicate
        so pale
        so pretty.
Primrose flowers are pin or thrum – gender balanced.
Primroses are politically correct.

Primroses withstand perishing spring weather.
Primroses point the way to perfection.

Qs
Quietly I grieve.
Quickly I write
questioning everything.
Quietly spring comes.
Quickly bracken unfurls
questioning nothing.
Quietly we die.
Quickly we forget
questioning everything.
How quick we are to question quietness.

Rest
Resting on water
I realise
recreation is possible.

I remember
a red coat
red lips.

Roots grow slowly
reaching inexorably
into rock.

Spring
Between squalls
the sun sometimes
shrugs, shuffles in,
soothing.

Sepals unsheathe,
shoots stretch.
Soon, soon,
a green sheen.

Time
trip plans
travel schedules
table of departures
terrorist clock
tormentor
tomorrow, petty pace
tribulation

Under
A woven coffin
carried by six
strong people,
living, crying.
We have put daffodils
into the earth.

Vim
After primroses come violets.
After wind comes velocity.
After wheels come vehicles.
After conviction comes vehemence.
After patience comes virtue.

Wonder
Wild wet wind in the wiggly woods.
A beetle's sunset-oil-sheen.
A fern unfurling.
A welter of questions about the world.

X-ray
A clot blocking one lung.
Advanced cancer.
No choice but exit.

Yes
You are young yet, she said, live on.
So: yeast, yacht and yellow flowers.

Zone
We go from zoology to zenith to zero.

Brian Hamill

A GOOD LISTENER

Sitting there and doing nothing – he was just staring out the window. It was a fair distance home so there was no point being impatient about it, the bus would stop as many times as it had to and people would get on and they would ask the driver stupid questions, does this one go to the hospital son, and people would be getting off and asking the driver stupid questions again, as if he gives a shite what happens once you step off that ledge, and so the thing would crawl all the way to the right stop, the right street, and that would be that. And tired anyway, too tired to get annoyed, because it took energy to get annoyed and he had none, it was these early mornings that did it, the body held up fine but just a weariness, that feeling in the head, his brain going slowly, as if everything was happening underwater, and affecting the eyes, his eyes that were starting to drop and it was only the early evening.

He became aware of a new noise, in between the sounds of the engine, of people coming in and going out, and the hissing of the door and the wind outside – somebody starting to speak. There had been no talk when he got on. One of those good journeys where there aren't any folk that know each other, so it stays quiet, tranquil, everybody sitting alone and just shutting up, but now there was this guy talking, steadily, bits of it could be heard as he blathered on and on.

Turning to look down the bus and seeing the guy immediately, the mouth going a mile a minute, blah blah, then stopping to grin, wink, enjoying his own joke, before going on with the stupid, shitty story. Something about a phonecall? An argument. Between him and his ex. About cigarettes, *her* cigarettes – it being much easier to pick the words up now that the fucker was in view.

And who is it he's talking to?

The girl, of course.

The girl that he must have turned round in his seat to strike up a conversation with, as she's in the one behind. Surely if he had known her, he'd be there on the one next to her? Nestled in together, surely.

As it is, they're neighbours, and only a few rows away. Her back, with the long hair coming down, then his face, grinning at her.

Continuing to watch them, casually. No need to try and hide it. He would keep an eye on them in fact, openly, to make sure there was nothing untoward. These young girls, alone, he had heard stories of what can happen. And there's something about the way the guy is looking at her. It doesn't sit right. He watches, unsure if the guy notices him or not.

The annoying thing about it is, he had actually noticed the girl as well when he got on – not getting any sort of a good look, but just the passing acknowledgement that the seat was occupied as he went past, and that the occupant appeared to be non-male. That's where it had ended for him – she was keeping herself to herself, so he did the same. It was a bus, it was a Tuesday, he wasn't going to slide up next to her as if they were in a cocktail bar.

But this young gun had.

Okay.

Rubbing his eyes, staring over at the two of them. Either this guy had only got on at the last stop, or worse, he'd spied her and moved over from somewhere else just to give her the chat. Her on the inside seat – is her head actually resting on the wall? It's tilted to the side. And the guy, on the opposite seat in front, turned right round with one leg poking out into the aisle.

Hard to tell if she's replying to him. Her ponytail twitches about at the back of her head, but that's the motion of the bus. It proved nothing.

The patter this guy was coming out with, it was not real. The feeling of being embarrassed for him, of getting a hotness about your own fucking ears and face, and then shaking the head and having to look away for a minute, mortified – and this for a person not even known to yourself. Crazy. That's how fucking bad it was, it was just terrible, what he was saying and how he was saying it. That this cunt could keep a straight face!

And there's no way in this world she doesn't know what he's up to. It was impossible not to, an absolute impossibility, there was not a fucking mammal on land that couldn't have, no no no.

No.

He looks across at an old man sitting opposite, and rolls his eyes. The old man nods, puts his head down. The couple are out of sight, but still he can hear the patter. It is not stopping.

These are the times where it's good to not be a lassie, to never have to put up with this kind of shite, this just transparent insulting fucking rubbish.

The temptation to shout something.

It's just the guy's laughing, leering fucking face. He's looking right at her, this young pervert, right now – for God's sake – his head, getting ever closer. The eyes he keeps giving her, it's obvious to the point of actually being threatening. They were moving about on her, burrowing into her. Even he could see that and he was several rows further back.

If only a message could be relayed to the guy somehow. Maybe to his phone, or into a fucking earpiece, something in real-time just to say to him, to tell him so that he would know: LISTEN, YOU'RE DOING TERRIBLE MATE, TERRIBLE, SHE'S EMBARRASSED, AND WE'RE EMBARRASSED AS WELL, COZ YOU'RE GIVING US ALL A BAD NAME HERE. TOO, TOO BAD. SERIOUSLY NOW, JUST FUCK OFF, OKAY, LEAVE IT. LEAVE IT AND COUNT YOURSELF LUCKY. FUCK OFF.

If only.

But still they're speaking, at least he is, when more people come in, some going upstairs and some sitting down here. This big, heavy-looking older woman parking herself in the chair in front – he has to move out to the aisle seat just to keep a bloody view of them, because of this old dame's big head with the hair all piled up and this hat perched on top of it, ridiculous, but quickly able to see them again . . . and having to blink and strain the eyes for a second to be sure, to see it clearly, but aye, it's there, it was happening, the fucking bastard had snaked his hand over the top of the seat and left it dangling down on her side. Fucking unbelievable! The fingers, so close to her, a trap, an invasion, but more than that – it's nothing but a pot-hole away from full fake-accidental hand-to-tit contact.

It is too much. Too much.

He takes a long breath in.

The bus was swaying round corners, but managing to hold the handrails and get down to where they are and seeing her wee face for the first time, she was quite young as expected, and so saying to him,

Right, RIGHT – to get him to look up, then going on: You leave the lassie alone, right? RIGHT? Don't give me any shite – and actually having to shout a bit coz of the engine noise – DON'T even try it, you never got on with her, you're annoying her and you're annoying me, so go, go wait at the door, you're getting off at the next stop.

His mouth moves in response, but not even listening, not to any of it, the face surely telling him his words weren't being heard, whatever daft shite he was saying, that it was just sound in a vacuum. Instead moving forward to grab a handful of the bastard's t-shirt, trying to pull him off the bloody seat, but then she says something too and that seems to work, he reacts to her words. Whatever she says. He holds his hands up then squeezes out, taking care not to make any contact, and going on down to where the door is. When he gets there he gives this look back, this nasty look with the lips moving again, and there's a second or two when the thought passes through – the thought that maybe he shouldn't be getting off so lightly. Maybe he is getting off way too light here. And there's still time. The driver was not slowing.

But it's the tiredness.

It's still there, he can feel it, there in his arms, his shoulders, his eyelids, even his knees and his hips, like he was an old man, ready for the fucking glue factory, and is this guy even worth it anyway, when he had already shit himself and went to leave, he was nothing, this guy, he was worse than nothing in fact. He was much worse.

And anyhow – the girl!

He turns and smiles, and she is speaking, so the smart move is to sit down, to listen, because she can't be heard as it is, so noisy on this fucking bus, all the sounds, all of them, and at the same fucking time, it's just too noisy. It is.

I know, she says. I know.

And I'm sorry about that. But I could tell that he was over trying his luck. I saw you were sitting minding your own business when I got on.

He was okay, she says.

The hiss of the doors again, and that moment, the beauty of it, when, even without looking, the guy can be seen, having almost forgot him as soon as he was out of sight, but then the corner of the eye, down on the pavement, his stupid face, the open mouth, and the bus pulling away, so slow, the old bus, it's great that it's so slow, dragging it out, with him there beside her and the youngster stuck outside. He smiles down at the guy, who is making a gesture with his phone in his hand or something but it doesn't deserve a glance really, he looks so wee and pathetic out there, this young buck, the bold one, no longer important enough to stare at, not even to smile at and shout, *Enjoy the walk home, fucker! Bye-byeeeeee!*

The guy was lost from view. The bus, now roaring along a different street.

And here he is. Right in front of the lassie. Smiling.

Her hair is red, it's red! It had looked brown but now he's that close and it's red, the strands of it so light it's hard to believe he couldn't tell before. She seems to be smiling too. This strange expression on her face.

Oh, was he okay? Well maybe he was but still, that's how it starts, eh?

She nods.

Now sitting on the chair that had been his, the young guy's, but with the hands holding firmly to the top of it, not right over on the other side. Her side. Not to be going about it like that.

I've seen him on here before, you know, doing that same thing to other people, you know, trying that old carry-on.

She shrugs, glances at the mobile she's slid out of her trouser pocket. The screen stays dark.

You off home then?

Aye. She doesn't look up. And thanks.

Or it sounded like she said thanks, but her voice was that quiet, so quiet it was hardly anything. It was tricky to know for sure.

He lowers his head, just a bit closer, so that the next thing she says will definitely be picked up.

Did you say thanks there? Was that it?

RIGHT.

But it was another voice. Coming from further up the bus.

Somebody stood in front of the back window. Right at the centre of it, the end of the aisle. The person – it is a male – and this male being there seems to make the light from the window stronger on either side of him. Squinting to try and see the face but it is not clear. He is too much in the shadow.

As the person gets closer he speaks again.

Right, you can leave the lassie alone, RIGHT? Don't even give me any shite. I saw you going over there when her pal was getting off, you're . . .

He smiles up at the guy. Ridiculous. It was. He doesn't say anything back. The guy is right by the seat. He stands. The guy is shouting.

The words aren't being heard now. It is just noise.

The guy is so close that he can feel the breath on his face, but he doesn't move.

There is the drift from air from one of the side-windows. The girl's hand on the cuff of his jacket briefly.

All the tiredness is gone. He is like stone. And still the new guy is talking. Watching his lips and teeth and tongue as they move. Then looking up – looking him in the eye. Straight in the eye. He is staring directly into that black dot in the middle of it.

There and nowhere else.

The talk keeps going. The lassie too.

He can sense the guy starting to back off. There is distance between them again. Another hand is on his wrist.

And he hears nothing.

Lydia Harris

GOAT: AN ASSAY

The bell round your neck
chimes to the creeping willow;
chimes underground
where the water you turn into milk
scrambles and rises.

In summer old women in scarves
finger your ears as if they were spindles.

Your bleat is a crimped linen collar.
Lappets hang from your chin.
You sprout hair on your belly.

You teach me the way of hard beds,
of paths through the snow-line.
You with your warm knobs of horn
and eyes like gall-spangles.

You rescue our wild, rocky places,
will not yield your milk to a stranger.
There's no pit of fire or ice
your cries can't transfigure.

Sarah Isaac

STALKING DEER

Matthew watched Rafe and the others stoop and disappear through the metal banded door of their castle, their height mocking the building's inferior dimensions. He was conscious of his inexperience at places like this. The doorway would accommodate him without his having to lower his head.

'We'll start with the guns,' Cameron said, steering Matthew away from warmth and succour, a proprietorial arm tight on his elbow. 'We'll make a hunter of you.'

A bone-shaking drive on a rough track followed. In the back of the Land Rover Cameron's son played on his mobile phone, beeping and squeaking. Grey clouds scudded above bare hills littered with boulders. The heather was dull, dark, not fully in flower yet. There were lines of stones and roofless, mean cottages. Matthew felt a lurch in his stomach and an unexpected longing for streetlights, for litter and signage. 'Always aim in a safe direction. Always unload your rifle before entering a building,' Cameron said.

There were other things Matthew must always do, a litany to recite before he was allowed to hold the weapon, which was surprisingly light and smelt of machine oil.

A rusted silhouette of a metal deer stood more than a hundred metres away. A birch tree on the horizon line curled away from the winds. Dressed entirely in camouflage, as if he were about to conduct a live-action round of *Call of Duty*, Cameron's son stuck a piece of paper onto the two-dimensional deer, marking the heart and the lungs. The target and the young man's face were tiny distant things, flickering white.

Matthew looked through the scope and the boy's pale eyes, his rictus of a grin, became clear. Matthew looked back to the hill behind, imagining a sniper there, him in the cross hairs, the target his back.

He'd lied to Betsy. Matthew had ostensibly been a vegetarian for the duration of their courtship, his meat-eating conducted illicitly, a handful of ham from the butcher's shoved in his mouth on the way home from work, sometimes a branded cheeseburger the size of his palm, slick with grease. Lately, that close-fleshed texture, the smell, had repelled him but he couldn't be a vegetarian here, on a corporate jolly in the Highlands with men who, although not senior to him, had the makings of it, that easy, loose-limbed confidence, that swagger.

His shots were conscious and precise. The ear defenders made them sound as if they came from elsewhere, from someone else.

Matthew felt the weight of Cameron's hands on his shoulder, congratulating him, and he didn't buckle.

The Land Rover pulled over a few miles further on. A group of stags were gathered in the lee of a dun-coloured hill.

'You can get up close and personal now,' Cameron said, 'get to know them. You won't be wanting them seeing you tomorrow.'

His son vaulted the gate, boots bristling with laces like whiskers, as if his feet had become beasts. A sack was slung across his back.

'Too much of a hurry, that boy,' Cameron said. 'Not sure he'll ever have the patience for this.'

The boy strode across the rutted ground as Cameron opened the gate. The stags watched as the boy spread the sack's contents across the ground.

'They're farmed?'

Matthew had been sold this as an encounter with the truly wild.

Cameron shook his head.

'It's not enough feed to keep them alive but enough that we'll know where to find them tomorrow.'

As the boy stepped back the stags moved forward, the largest advancing beyond the line of feed that halted the rest and forced them into a ragged geometry. The animal carried on walking towards Cameron and Matthew and raised his head. Its antlers were a forest of points. It was as if it had grown in those few paces forward.

Cameron loaded his rifle.

'Getting ahead of himself, that one,' he said. 'It pays to be ready.'

The stag's chest was thick. There was copper in his coat. Thick fur coursed over his neck. The stag opened its mouth and bellowed, then took another step forward, lowering its head and making it into a weapon, a mass of points that could bruise and pierce.

The stag lifted a hoof and scraped it across the ground. Some of the feeding stags lifted their heads and began to push through the uneven line. 'You wait,' Cameron said to his son, who was already back at the vehicle, a gun in his hands, 'you wait.'

The gamekeeper held his arms wide and his head down as if he were ready to butt against the hard points of the stag's antlers.

Cameron bellowed back at the stag, louder than it, the sound bouncing around them. Then he lifted his gun, all the while staring at the beast a few yards in front. The stag rubbed its hoof over the dry ground one more time and rolled its head, lips curled back over large square teeth.

In the safety of the Land Rover Matthew could feel the beat of his heart. He let his shoulders fall and unclenched his fists.

'We could have him tomorrow,' the son said.

'Not for a few years yet,' his father said.

Whitewashed outbuildings spattered with lichen huddled at the rear of the castle. The Land Rover pulled up next to the most considered and tallest outbuilding, an octagonal tower built from dressed stone.

'Davey's got one from this morning. You'll see the whole thing.'

The gamekeeper kept his hand on Matthew's back, steering him to an open door from which thick ribbons of clear plastic hung. The son sloped off, the phone back in his hands, his fingers typing.

Matthew was reminded then that this place was a business, that he and the others were only temporary stewards, whatever connections Rafe claimed to this 'estate'.

The smell that greeted them was rich and dense, a condensation of every butcher's shop and unwashed dog that Matthew had ever encountered. He had preferred to buy meat prepacked in the supermarket, sliding out steaks from plastic trays with a minimum of physical contact, averting his eyes from the rivulets of blood left. He had liked his meat to be prepared by someone else, curried or stewed out of recognition. And now he preferred not to eat it at all.

The floor was painted blood-red. The corpse of a stag lay on a table. It was more worn-looking than the stag that had bellowed at them, darker, the coat scarred. Its hind legs were tied and suspended from a hook, making it looked draped, like an overlong curtain.

Matthew's Virgin Rail croissant-and-coffee deal shifted and stirred in his stomach. He breathed through his mouth.

'You'll get used to it,' Cameron said. 'We're conservationists, that's what you need to remember. We're protecting these hills. We're protecting these beasts.'

A red tongue lolled from a pink mouth. There was already a slit in the stag's belly, an empty, shadowed space there.

'That's the field dressing, a gralloch we call it, the insides left on the hill so the meat stays clean. The hawks will see to the waste. You'll see tomorrow, maybe give it a try.'

An aproned man came from the adjoining room, a sharp knife held in strong hands. Davey sawed away at the stag's neck, the antlers clattering against the hard surfaces.

Matthew kept his eyes fixed at a point just below the stag's head until it fell away and Davey placed it to one side, the eyes still open, the tongue still lolling.

Matthew tried to pretend he was watching one of those crime programmes Betsy liked where corpses were invaded by gloved hands that sawed, stitched, measured and weighed.

The headless carcass was ratcheted up so it hung, swaying then settling. Davey peeled away the pelt as if it were simply a coat the stag had borrowed. Matthew tried not to think about his own flesh and blood, the ligaments and tendons bright red beneath his well-nourished, tended skin. Still he didn't heave, didn't lean against the cold wall and slide down it until his elbows rested on his knees and he could put his fists in his eyes and sob.

'Just tired mate,' he said to Rafe when they sat in baronial splendour in the dining room. He pushed his meat under uneaten vegetables and tried to ignore the ranks of dead stags arrayed on the wall, watching them chew. Some of the dead heads were just bones and antlers, their eye-sockets dark and round.

His bedroom was away from the others, a low-ceilinged attic room, the bed small. He wanted to talk to Betsy, to explain. The surrounding hills blocked all reception. He scrolled through his photos, him and Betsy smiling and found himself mimicking that expression – except, in this cold, damp room, it felt more like a grimace.

Breakfast was a buffet. Matthew piled a plate with beans and tomatoes, mushrooms, a slice of toast. Rafe joined him, idly picking up a glistening sausage and biting it, the fat moist on his lips. He sniffed the air around Matthew as if he was a predator and Matthew the prey.

'You remembered then. Today we are scentless.'

Without hair gel Rafe looked older. He sucked his fingers and took another sausage, his eyebrows raised at Matthew's meat-free plate.

Davey drove, just him, Matthew, Rafe and Cameron's son in the Land Rover. The others were going in a different direction with Cameron. Davey and Rafe talked quietly in the front. In the back, next to Matthew, Cameron's son played with his phone, his presence hot and restless. Then they walked, Davey and Cameron's son striding ahead, the camouflage they wore absorbing them into the hill, making Matthew worry. He'd be lost without them. But then the keepers would wait on the brow of the next horizon, snickering at the incomers' lack of fitness.

The wind dropped and a dark cloud of midges surrounded them, nuzzling Matthew's eyelids and nipping his nostrils, mocking his efforts to chase them away. Heather scratched through his trousers, multipurpose things that Rafe, in his knee-length argyle socks and tweed knickerbockers, had mocked. The convoluted roots of the heather hid unknown chasms that, more than once, sent him plummeting to the ground. He was breathless and tired. There was an ache in his hips he'd never felt before and still Rafe smiled and whispered about the 'elemental nature' of it.

Finally, Davey signalled, waving his arm then lowering his palm down. They fell to their hands and knees, first crawling, then, for the last few yards, elbowing their way over the scrub in what Rafe had called last night 'The Revenant moment'. It was a film that had enthralled Matthew. Betsy had railed against the way the women were either dead, mad or whores. She'd predicted the end and cried at the unnecessary death of the horse.

Below them, shifting slowly through rough grass, instead of buffalo there were deer.

Rafe loaded his rifle and Davey, using his binoculars, pointed out the stag he was to aim for. At the opposite edge of the group there was a bigger stag. Rafe whispered to Davey, taking something from his pocket and pressing it into his hand. Cameron's son sniggered softly. Rafe's gun swung to the right, to that redder, royal stag. Matthew could see that this didn't follow the rules Cameron had impressed on him. Hinds were gathered around the stag. There wasn't a clear shot. Rafe fired, the noise a crack carried by the wind. A hind fell, blood blossoming on her stomach, her legs folding under her. She raised herself and buckled again like a shopgirl awash with vodka on a night out. The stag turned and bounded away. The rest of the deer scattered, then slowed and stopped, still, just, in shooting distance. Matthew watched Rafe swing his rifle back to that first stag. He and Davey fired together. The stag fell onto its side, its weight making it roll. The hind, Davey's kill, tottered and crumpled.

They stumbled down the hill, Rafe gleeful, waving the rifle as if it were a branch he had gathered, thumping Matthew on the back.

They watched Davey stick a knife into the stag's throat, working the blade in to its hilt. Blood, coppery and warm, gushed out, staining the paler fur of the creature's throat. The gamekeeper pressed his boot on the beast's belly, pumping it to release more blood that pooled around their boots. Then the boy put his hand into the wound and pulled out the bloodied windpipe, scraping it until a section was ringed white, cutting and knotting it while Davey sawed carefully through skin and fur, cutting from the rectum to the centre of the stag's belly, his hands and wrists red. He eased out the stomachs gently, translucent white sacs marbled with fat that caught the light, that shifted and moved. Matthew looked away, tracking the living deer making their way back into the hills. The hairs on the back of Matthew's neck rose. There was still that feeling of being watched.

They tied the stag's hooves and Cameron's son and Rafe began the laborious task of dragging the stag's body to a point where the Land Rover could reach it. Davey saw to the hind with the same efficiency.

'Canny bastard, that stag we missed,' he said. 'Still, his turn will come.'

There was half an hour of pulling the bodies before they reached a place the Land Rover could reach. The scent of the dead deer travelled with them. Flies gathered. Finally, they reached clear, flat ground. While Davey and the boy washed their hands in a shallow stream, Rafe leant on a boulder and lifted his head to the sky, his arms folded across his chest.

'I told you,' he said. 'Didn't I? Fucking marvellous. It makes you feel so . . . alive.'

Matthew drank water and looked at the rope burns on the palms of his hands, felt the ache in the small of his back. He felt as if he had lost some part of himself, was barely alive at all.

The slow, deep rumbling that sounded as if it were coming from under the ground stopped Rafe elaborating. It gave Matthew a reason not to reply. It made them all pause. The heather wavered as if there were a heat haze. The sky was shades of violet and grey, a mirror of the ground beneath and sunless. There was no approaching thunderstorm. There was no nearby battlefield, no approach of jet planes practising the terrorising of the Middle East.

The men dressed in splatters of green and grey looked up.

Deer lined the horizon. There were hundreds of them. The sight reminded Matthew of long-ago Western films, cowboys or cavalry unexpectedly surrounded by mounted Indians, hopelessly outnumbered. He could almost hear the hysterical 'whoop, whoop' of the Apache, a Sioux or a Cree war cry.

It was a peculiar time to be remembering the names of native American tribes, to be grateful for remembering the right nomenclature. He recalled Becky's sweet smile and her constant gentle corrections when he slipped into political incorrectness. He put his hand to his mouth and trapped one small quiet wail, then another. He wished for a feather in a hairband, charcoal to mark his face, some way of letting the mass of assembled deer know he was their kindred spirit, not one of these men with their hardware and their hand-made socks costing more than a hundred pounds a pair.

Some of the deer coughed and shifted from side to side. Davey loaded his gun. Rafe and Cameron's son followed suit. The deer made their way down the hill, gathering speed. Cameron's son fired first, repeating shots that were too soon and too high. The men expected their following shots to make the herd part and run either side of them. They expected themselves to have the inanimate strength of boulders, of trees.

Matthew lay down, held his hands over his head and waited for the beat of hooves to press him to the ground, to lay him flat, to split his gut. He heard hooves drumming and groans and yells and the cracking of sticks, perhaps of bones. He smelt heather and deer and shit and other fleshly things. He smelt his own sweat. He watched a bee fly away and he heard the rumble of hooves grow soft. He looked at the structure of the heather blossom and counted the purple lobes on a single sprig. He tested things out piecemeal, his toes, his fingers, his ankles, his knees, until he was sure he could move. He felt his mouth with numb fingers, checking his teeth and it seemed he was all there, the blood on his jacket borrowed. Finally, he stood up.

The mess a herd of deer could make of a man was more brutal, more obliterating than the shooting and eviscerating of the stag. There was nothing resembling Rafe left to stuff, to mount on a shield, to hang above a dining table. Davey was almost indistinguishable from the heather and the rock. Cameron's son had become longer and leaner.

It was Betsy, that's what had saved him. It was surely that and his part-time, indifferent vegetarianism, the fact that this was not his land, nor his gun. And he hadn't fired, hadn't shot anything living. He looked up to the sky, blue now, bright, the clouds casting moving shadows; and then he saw it, standing on the brow of the hill. The stag's antlers were a silhouetted corona, his posture regal. It was grander than Landseer's stag, than the stuffed stags that had stared at Matthew in the dining room. It was noble, like Bambi's father had been, silhouetted against flames. It was a special moment; a connection Matthew could talk about when he described his miraculous escape.

There was no preamble to the stag's charge.

Matthew's last moments were purely olfactory, blood, shit, piss, all of them his.

Andy Jackson

I FEEL LOVE (DISCO BISCUITS #1)

You phoned to ask me *did you feel the quake?*
It's on the local news. I felt the lifting of the day,
the swell of sunlight as I came awake,
rising to periscope depth, imagining the way
it must have been; oh yes, a minor shock,
but still enough to strum the tensioned wires
that strung our muted telephones, knock
out the power, set bells swinging in the shires.
Somehow all the old topography had changed,
and so I lay in wait for other freak events,
the *force majeure,* the aftershocks, the strange
vibrations of the world, its perfect accidents.
In time, one of us will map this land alone;
till then, come over, bring everything you own.

Nadine Aisha Jassat

AUNTIE

When I was young, I spent a lot of time under the wing of my father's oldest sister. Auntie Khutch was a schoolteacher, and a strong matriarch like her mother and aunt before her. We'd go everywhere together; if she went to the grocer, there'd be my face pressed against the counter below her. If she went visiting, there'd be my shoes on the welcome mat next to hers. She was a religious woman, and many nights I'd fall asleep on the sofa to the sound of her whispering duas, and the rock of prayer beads working in her hands, as gentle and as steady as the breath of the sea meeting the roll of coastal pebbles. Click, click, click. I didn't think much about God, but enjoyed the white prayer scarf she gave me, embroidered with delicate flowers and framing my face in clean, smooth lines. I liked being part of her spiritual world, a space only I was invited to share, mirroring her with my small body. It was as if once we put on our scarves we were, somehow, no longer ourselves but two snow-topped mountains, her movements surrounding us as calm and as regular as the tide. Even now it is so easy to lean back and conjure up the sounds of her: the rustle of fabric as she knelt in prayer, hands coursing the velveteen mat, breath through lips, and the dance of bracelets up and down her wrist, a gentle rhythm.

One day, as I accompanied her dutifully, she asked if I could hear the Azan. I had been listening to its music without question; undulating and familiar, it rolled through the window with the breeze. Without turning from my task – for my aunt was always very industrious, and I was never in want of useful activity – I replied, 'Yes, Auntie, it is a beautiful bird.' Of course, my aunt found this hilarious, and repeated the tale with much humour, adopting my small voice in the same way I twirled in her saris, amused at her niece mistaking the call to prayer that rung across the city as the song of a treasured bird.

As I grew older, the space between our shadows grew further apart – marked by geography. Hers rests in a southern corner of Africa, and mine stretches over the cobbles and paving-stones of Scotland's capital. There are no Azans here, but I search for my auntie in the shop windows of Leith Walk, brightly coloured fruits displayed in crates and packs like marbles. I work here, made my home here, but not a week goes by without me missing the click, click, click of her, like a timepiece to my life. The other day, someone asked me what I had done for Eid, and I told them about the pictures my family had sent from far away through their smartphones – '*a looker phone, Auntie, a looker!*' – of the festivities they had prepared. I feast with my eyes, I joked, all the while feeling the silence, homesick for my half-home. I wanted to tell them that Eid feels homeless here. There is no-one like us, nor was there in the last place. But there are things we do not say. Still, I enjoy being around people my aunt would have found kinship with – in her friendly and dutiful manner. I imagine the conversations they would have, hear her exchanging salaams, haggling in her blunt and authoritative way. 'Now you listen here,' she'd say, and I do.

I do not think she would feel free here, though, in the same way that Britain sits on me like a favourite jumper: I do not wish to take it off, but every so often it chafes at the neck. She visited, once, when I was in school, but today's Britain is not the same as she left it. A change has been growing in the wind here, blowing through with the newspapers in the streets. We have words for things I'd never heard of as a child now, and fears we'd never dreamt of before. Where at primary school I was marched onto the assembly stage, in my checked cotton dress and pressed socks, to talk about being Muslim, my brother – younger by seven years – was asked not about the Quran but my dad's gun collection, and whether he owned an AK47. 'They're going to blow us up,' they said. But it was us sweeping the rubble of broken glass from our living room floor, and I fear we will be sweeping still for a long time to come.

My partner is from here – a good man, the kind of man who forgets my mother's name but listens to every word she says. He met my auntie only once, and said he was surprised how alike we were, how we moved in the same ways. But there is a distance between us. As we watch the news in our sunny seaside flat, in the background footage of a report about terror – the surrounding shots, the scene setters – I see two Muslim men greeting each other, *As-Salaam-Alaikum*. As the syllables of response bloom on my tongue, I wonder what these words mean to my partner, what thoughts he tastes when he hears them. It was at that moment that I realised, just as the shadows between Auntie and me had grown, so too would the shadow of my own child be separate from me. And I felt sad, then, heavy and accepting, for the child who would never have the space to listen to the Azan, and hear the call of a free bird.

Brian Johnstone

THE ARTHUR'S SEAT COFFINS

In late June 1836, a group of boys discovered a small cave in the rock,
hidden behind three pointed slabs of slate. Concealed within were *17
miniature coffins*.—National Museums Scotland

The hand that laid these figures out,
cached in a nest of rock, is as unknown
as their purpose. Of near a score unearthed

no more than eight remain, each casket
gouged from a single plank by the heft
of a cobbler's knife. Stood open to admire

like childhood treasures, the trinkets
they contain: toy dolls, all soldiers once;
painted boots still on their feet; the marks

of helmets on their heads. But each
is geared for civvy street, in day clothes,
checks and cotton prints, plain weave,

yet every suit bespoke. The same hand
surely pieced these garments up, sucked
thread ends the better to pass them through

the needle's eye, and tugged at three-ply,
threading stitches into cloth. Took steps
to place these men, each one rescued

from rank and file, back in accustomed life.
No prick of pins, no witchery, no harm.
Only the quiet comfort of the grave.

Lis Lee

ROAD ENDING

Baseball glove or brown owl? I flinched though I was inside my car. It was an owl, pitching sideways over caramel winter bracken. I braked, pulled into a passing place, turned off the engine, wound down my window, inhaled ozone. Once it made me dizzy. Visiting years later, I remembered.

An old man used to live close to this place on a raised beach, a chin on the west face of the island. Blackhouse ruins bristle here, stubble on a turf cheek. The man had a pet owl. That was the craic after the burial. We hadn't known about it until he died.

Duncan Mhor would mount guard at his road end, a scarecrow wearing a hat, earflaps akimbo like a cormorant's drying wings. His greatcoat was belted with twine and his army boots had no laces. He would adze down the hooked, fractured path from his cottage, whatever the weather and stand, staring one way then the other.

His road end was where I saw him when I drove past to my own slice of bog. Tar whelks pinned his track to the single-track road alongside a gravel bar where road menders took their break and leaned for tea.

His marshmallow house gripped hill rock with split log toenails, softened in Atlantic rain baths and long past the dryness for burning. The house wept roof slates and shed shards of whitewash. It seemed to be melting. Sash windows boxed postcard panoramas of a loch whose mouth spat rock incisors and bit the island almost in half.

Duncan fought in the Second World War and returned to become a recluse. It was public isolation. The island hinted signs of occupation in children who keeked out of doorways and men who rode tractors on never-level fields. Caravans were home to the homeless; broken down cars, windows punched out, were kennels to the kennel-less. Washing lines of nappies gave away secret women when rain held off.

Herons with legs like scissors still share spring tide shores with hunched gatherers, Quasimodos turning over rocks and searching with cold, wet fingers for apocryphal heaps of whelks that might be swept up with a broom. Aye.

Duncan never married. He stopped working the croft after the war. His parents had died. Ribs of ragwort bearing a dusting of gold medals were easy in his fields. Lichen-mapped boulders huddled in low heaps, wall duty done.

A cockerel with a crow-green tail and a few toffee hens used to feed on the hill with black-faced sheep and dun rabbits on summer days. The hens roosted among wee purple ballet-dancers in a fuchsia hedge that clung with stout brown arms to a grey wall. In the old garden, rare pink montbretia poked from a sphagnum loofah. The birds perished, their foolish roost a larder for polecats the colour of badgers.

I called at Duncan's from time to time and left him eggs from my own hens. I repaired the green wooden mailbox at the road end so that his bread and cheese, left by the travelling grocer, stayed dry and were safe from sheep and ravenous sheepdogs. They eat shit, a New Age traveller told me. I knew.

If the old man hadn't been seen by anyone for a few days I climbed the hill. Duncan never invited me in. I satisfied myself that he was upright, dressed and pink.

On a January day, when he hadn't been seen at his post for a week, I tacked in stiff oilskins through horizontal sleet and chapped at his door. There was no answer so I pushed my way in. Duncan was slumped in a sagging armchair, wearing his greatcoat and hat. His boots lay on their sides on a cold range, rows of nail heads in the soles like a currant grin on a gingerbread man.

The room was freezing and smelled of mould. A table was frosty with used crockery. A bed in one corner was undressed, the mattress gaudy with sepia stains. A high tide of blankets congealed on the linoleum floor.

Duncan was gasping, his eyes closed. The skin on his cheek was cold as sand. I dragged a blanket over and as I was wrapping him I heard a shifting, a soft-shoe shuffle in the hall. It was an owl, set on the banister, an ill-placed piece of taxidermy with real eyes. Guano was cemented to the floor below. Chipolatas of fur, embedded with small teeth and bones, lay about.

I opened the door to the white outside and clapped my hands. The owl looped down with a dry snap, brushing my face, and for a moment was framed like a crucifix in the doorway.

The sun shone the day we sank Duncan. The granite church was built on bedrock lapped by bog. Gravestones heeled over. Waterlogged topsoil gagged on coffins. Grass paths would rise and fall, tamped down by mourners' feet. John Smith's grave on Iona was just the same.

The wake was held in a neighbour's kitchen. Winter woollens were steaming over an oil-fired range. We talked about old Duncan, Duncan Mhor, the Gaelic speaker who went to war and came back broken. Befriended an owl. Aye.

Wes Lee

BODY, DID YOU KNOW

Body, did you know? Like the mother
who kept her head in the sand.
Lung were you aware, heart did you witness, throat
were you looking through the screen door,
bone did you leap to a window, kneecap
were you crouched behind the couch, low, trembling
and rib having just come running in from
the garden, stopped (an armful of lilacs),
socket did you see, but swivel
and lips did you open in a gasp then press
and shoulders did you turn then sag,
hairline did you flinch back,
skin did you feel the cold from an open window
and suddenly shiver (the curtain transform
and seem to be a curtain in a dream),
tongue did you get a taste then swallow
and jaw did you drop then clamp shut
and neck did you forget for a second
your graceful tilt?

Joan Lennon

ICARUS' MOTHER

She'd kept his room just as it had been –
just as it should be.
'You're home now,' she told him,
as she swept the last of the sea sand
from the floor,
shut the curtains
against the sun's siren stare –
'That's quite enough of that' –
and hung him neatly in the wardrobe.

Robin Lloyd-Jones

CHECKING OUT THE CZECHS WITH JACKSON

'How about we check out the Czech Republic this time?' Jackson suggests over Skype, he in Hawaii, me in Scotland. I had met Jackson several years earlier. I had gone to Honolulu for a conference and, in the days immediately after it, had taken a three-day cruise round some of the other hundreds of islands that make up the Hawaiian archipelago. Jackson had been living on Oahu – the island on which Honolulu is situated – for two years and thought it was time he saw the neighbouring islands of Molokai, Lanai, Maui and Big Island, so had signed up for the same cruise. Although there was a forty-year age gap between us, we immediately bonded. He had issues with his own father and was looking for some kind of replacement father-figure. There is something flattering, I suppose, in being looked up to, although, since he was six foot six, I was also looked down on. Jackson was a super fit mass of bulging muscles. I recall, on my second visit to Hawaii, returning after several hours of paddling with Jackson in a big swell. While I was only too glad to take a long rest, Jackson went straight off to his local gym for a 'proper workout' lifting heavy weights.

Jackson is an ex-US Marine who had been a sniper in the Iraq war. In modern warfare, killing the enemy is often done at a distance. The rockets, bombs and shells hit their target but you don't see, close up, their effect. It's different for a sniper. Through your telescopic sights you see another human being's head explode as a direct result of your action. This and the stress of hiding out in enemy territory for days on end finally got to Jackson. He was invalided out of the army with Post-Traumatic Stress Disorder. Sharing his apartment with him, sharing a hotel room with him, I saw something of how awful this can be: Jackson would wake up in the night screaming and covered in sweat; I might find him weeping quietly in a corner somewhere; or out of nowhere might come a sudden fit of shaking and anxiety. Mostly, he is a quiet, pleasant, gentle, smiling person. In the First World War they called his condition shell shock, or simply plain cowardice, for which a soldier might be shot. At least Jackson is getting help and treatment at the military hospital.

We meet at Prague airport. I nurse my hand in the taxi, following his crushing handshake. Why do I never learn? Jackson flourishes his copy of *The Beer Guide to Prague: Over Seventy of the Best Beer Experiences in Prague* and talks enthusiastically about the city's many pubs and beer cellars and the fact that it has more breweries per head of population than any other city in the world.

'The best beer in Europe!' he declares.

'Some of the best architecture, too,' I say, thinking of my guidebook, rather different from his, packed with information about cathedrals, castles, old churches, museums and art galleries.

It works out quite well, actually. Some days we cater for callow youth; other days we have what Jackson calls 'wrinkly time.' We alternate between beer experiences and culture fixes. Nearly a hundred different beers to sample in shades ranging from black to gold, and a thousand years of architecture: Romanesque, Gothic, Medieval, Renaissance, Baroque, Soviet Realism and some extra-ordinary modern buildings all side by side – Prague, in Middle Europe, the centre of the old kingdom of Bohemia where East meets West, where the onion domes of Orthodox churches vie for attention with the imposing seats of power of the Hapsburgs and the Austro-Hungarian Empire.

'You've written much more about the culture stuff than about the beer,' Jackson complains when I show him my notes.

'Well, to be honest, Jackson, things get a bit hazy after the first pint or two.'

Our hotel room overlooks a sea of terracotta tiled roofs in varying shades of weathered red and pink. Spires and towers break the skyline. Prague is known as 'the city of a hundred towers' and from the window of the Hotel Marcello, near the city centre, I can see that this is no exaggeration. Jackson has the ability to make any room seem small, particularly when he is swinging heavy oak chairs, one in each hand, in lieu of dumbbells. He is wearing his 'Bad Toro' t-shirt, which I bought for him on a previous trip together. I forget how many Xs came before the L, but it was the biggest size they had and it stretches tight across his massive chest. He empties the fridge, unplugs it and heaves it onto the back of his shoulders.

'I'm just going to run up and down the stairs a few times,' he says. Perhaps I should mention we're on the fourth floor.

When I hear him returning, only slightly out of breath, I drop to the floor in the push up position.

'Ninety-seven, ninety-eight . . .' I intone as he enters.

'Wow, Robin! Good job!'

Such trust, such innocence. I feel bad.

Prague is a magical maze of winding streets, filled with small cafés, restaurants and pubs with live jazz bands or gypsy musicians from nearby Hungary and Romania. In these cobbled warrens are the traditional black theatres, with puppets, masked figures and shadow plays acting out dark tales. Every day we get lost, but to be lost in Prague is a total pleasure. Making a virtue out of our bumbling incompetence we adopt the philosophy of the *dérive* – the unplanned wander in which anything can happen and, when it does, you enjoy it to the full. The restaurants are big on meat – and beer, of course. Hardly a vegetable in sight.

At an open-air street-side restaurant we choose, from a longish menu, what is translated as 'pig's knee.' When the food arrives, each joint is the size of a football and most of it meat, not bone. I make minimal inroads into mine before admitting defeat, but Jackson rises to the occasion, getting himself on the outside of all of his and then the remains of mine, which is most of it. While we are digesting our meal, a troupe of Buddhist monks in saffron robes pass by, beating gongs.

'Have you heard the Dalai Lama joke?' I ask.

'No.'

'A man goes into a pizza parlour and says, "I'll have a Dalai Lama". The girl behind the counter looks blank. "You know", says the man, "One with everything."'

Jackson doesn't get it. In fact, the Dalai Lama didn't get it either when an interviewing journalist repeated it to him. 'What's a pizza parlour?' he wanted to know.

Jackson really comes into his own at 'El Toro', an Argentinean restaurant serving every possible variety of beef where, for a set amount, you can 'eat all you can eat.' Jackson clearly takes this as a personal challenge. Donning his Bad Toro t-shirt, he swaggers through the swing doors like John Wayne entering the Last Chance Saloon. Oh boy, did they make a loss that day!

So many places in Prague jostle to appear on these pages. Of these I will write not one word. I will leave it to the plethora of guidebooks and websites . . . Except, I can't resist a mention, a mere mention, mind you, of the Old Town Square in which stands the Old Town Hall, completed in 1338. Built into its Gothic tower is an astronomical clock, known as the Orloj, rich in intriguing symbols. On the hour, Death rings a bell and inverts his hour glass, and the Twelve Apostles parade past the windows above the clock, nodding to the crowd. Architecturally admirable though the square is, it's the people who throng it that are the attraction for me: buskers by the dozen, a booth performing a Czech version of Punch and Judy, wild music from a Romanian group with drums and bagpipes, frozen statues in gold or silver, a beturbanned man with a large python, acrobats and break-dancers and young tourists segwaying through the crowd with amazing skill. Oh, and I must slip in a few words about the medieval Charles IV bridge, a pedestrian bridge spanning the Vltava with its sixteen arches and lined with thirty baroque statues of saints.

I am lost again and go into a shop to ask for directions. The young woman signals to me to type in my question on her smart phone. The phone translates this into Czech and then translates her answer into English for me. It's the first time I've encountered this clever app – just one of the many ways modern technology is changing the travel experience. I'm so impressed that, when I get home, I obtain a similar app. It even speaks Klingon, which is going to be very useful.

We decide to sign up for a 'See Prague by Bicycle' tour, which promises to reach interesting places by cycle paths and narrow backstreets seldom used by cars. Things get off to a bad start. Even their largest bicycle is way too small for Jackson and it doesn't help that his considerable weight keeps pushing the saddle down to its lowest position. His knees are practically up to his chin and sticking out sideways. He wobbles all over the place, crashing into several fellow cyclists in our group of eight. I'm just as bad. Unaccountably, everything is a bit out of focus and I'm having trouble judging distances. Between us we wreak havoc, much to the despair of Carl, our young guide.

'I got tired of being a segway guide, so I switched to the bicycles,' Carl tells me, adding after yet another crash, 'Maybe I'll go back to the segways.' He peers closely at me. 'Those aren't sunglasses you're wearing, they're 3D cinema specs!'

When leaving home I must have grabbed the wrong pair from a collection of assorted glasses in my desk draw. Carl lends me a pair of proper sunglasses and tells Jackson not to bother with the saddle but to pedal standing up. With Jackson and me sorted out, the tour proceeds on a more even keel, so to speak.

Rising to the top of my mind, like cream, are two stopping-places on this tour. The Lennon Wall is in a secluded square opposite the French Embassy. When John Lennon was murdered in December 1980 he became a pacifist hero for many young Czechs. Somebody painted his image on the wall and it was soon joined by protest and pacifist graffiti. The Lennon Wall became a political focus for Prague youth. Despite frequent coats of whitewash, the communist police never managed to keep it clean for long. When communist rule ended in 1989, the messages became less political, but the tradition of writing on the wall remains, making it a multi-coloured blaze of signs, symbols, logos, names and messages of goodwill.

We arrive at the Memorial for the victims of Communism. Seven life-size bronze figures descend a flight of steps. The further up the steps the more the figures become disintegrated, losing limbs and their bodies breaking open. The figures represent the seven phases of a man living in a totalitarian state – as the Czechs did for forty-one years from 1948 to 1989. The gradual deterioration of each successive figure tells of the physical and mental destruction of many Czechs under an oppressive regime. Although Carl could hardly have been born when communist rule came to an end, he speaks passionately and vehemently about the oppression, the arrests, imprisonments, executions, forced exiles, the censorship and lack of freedom. Perhaps his parents and aunts and uncles had suffered under this heavy yoke.

'Český Krumlov – a medieval gem on the banks of a river,' so reads the brochure in the travel agency into which Jackson and I step after a leisurely coffee (me) and beer (Jackson) in the Old Town Square. The brochure goes on to describe Český Krumlov as 'One of the most beautiful historic towns in Europe' and its fairytale, red-roofed castle as 'the Pearl of the Renaissance, one of the most important historic sites in Central Europe'.

Český Krumlov is about three hours south of Prague, on the same Vltava river that flows through Prague, but upstream by some one hundred and seventy-three kilometres, a river that, further north in Germany, joins the Elbe, which finally reaches the North Sea at Hamburg.

'Let's go!' I urge.

'Yeah,' agrees Jackson. 'At least we can pronounce this one.'

Our hired car has an English-speaking SatNav – a real boon since all the signs and directions are in Czech. Jackson drives because he's used to driving on the right. After the first half hour I stop flinching at every roundabout and start enjoying the scenery. We pass through rolling agricultural land, a mixture of grass and bare stubble. The landscape is empty of life. No cattle in sight; none at all. Considering the amount of meat the Czechs eat, I can't account for this unless, of course, Jackson has eaten the lot. As our automatic Skoda purrs along almost silently, I regale Jackson with tales of my first car in the 1950s – no indicators, hand signals only; the headlight dipper was a button on the floor; only three gears; the noise inside the car so loud you had to shout to be heard; and, due to an innovative transversely mounted engine, it didn't go when it rained.

'I bet you don't even know the hand signal for "I am going to slow down."'

Jackson's disbelief turns to laughter and we miss a turning. Miss SatNav sounds disappointed in us.

We stop at a roadside restaurant for lunch. The menu is in Czech and the waiter doesn't speak English. He mimes the animal we are about to eat.

'It's got big ears!' Jackson shouts, enjoying the game of charades.

'Could be horns,' I say.

The waiter adds sound effects to his mime.

'OMG!' Jackson exclaims, 'It barks!'

'I think he might be coughing.'

The waiter's eyes light up. 'Coffee?'

Our order, when it arrives, turns out to be some kind of meat stew. What kind of meat we never found out.

Český Krumlov exceeds all expectations aroused by the brochure. Jackson is relaxed and hasn't had a nightmare for nearly a week. I've been hard on him, I know. He's neither the Philistine nor the beer-swilling hog I've portrayed him to be. At the airport Jackson extends his hand to shake mine. Instead, I give him a big hug.

Rose McDonagh

OWLETS

We had planned to paint the barn blue and call it a library. We couldn't find the key that first evening and so it was only on the second day that we discovered the nest. Above the central cross-beam, a thicket of pellets and feathers with two owlets in the centre of it, their faces like dandelions gone to seed. 'Well that's that out the window,' Jack said. I could not disagree; we couldn't disrupt them.

They were enchanting, like small supernatural beings. I'd think about them at night, the two pale spectres in the dark of the barn, there all the time, awake while we slept, the impossibility of knowing what it was like to be them. What did they sense, feel, see? What did they think, even, if such a term could be applied to them?

Jack had a friend of his from a wildlife society come and tag them and weigh them. I watched them being lifted from their nest-world by gloved hands, their beaks open in pink outrage. 'There are superstitions about owls, aren't there?' I said to Jack's friend.

'Yeah, barn owls predict a death in the household,' he said, and we both laughed in a nervy sort of way.

It was about two weeks after that when we heard about the missing girl. It was actually on the television news. Jack and I offered to be in a search party but the police didn't want that kind of thing so early on. Perhaps you can see where this is going. I am certain I checked the barn properly on that first day; I searched all the corners, lifted up old machinery she couldn't possibly be under. The place was empty. But come the following night, when I went to look at the owlets, there she was, sitting in the corner of the barn, the hood of her coat pulled down so it hung over her eyes. She was holding one of the baby owls. How she had got it out of the nest I do not know. There was no ladder. But there she sat, cradling it in her arms, the little thing hissing like a cat, the other in the nest looking on, watching the whole scene. There is a saying that an owl has *more the face of a Christian than a bird* and the one in the nest did have the look of a painted saint, peering down at the girl.

'What have you got there?' I said, though I knew exactly what she had.

She didn't respond. I took a step towards her. She kept her head down. What was I going to do? I couldn't snatch the owl from her; it might get injured. The little thing was hissing away at me.

'Please would you give the chick to me? They're delicate, they're awfully delicate. We wouldn't want it to get hurt and its mother will worry.'

She mumbled something.

I couldn't make it out.

'Please, give the owl to me.' I took another step towards her.

She muttered something again.

'I can't hear what you're saying.'

I knelt close to her.

'Don't phone the police,' she said.

'Ah I know, I know, but I'm probably going to have to, because everyone's been looking for you and we could get into trouble if we don't.'

She mumbled something else.

'What are you saying, dear?' I said. I was not in the habit of calling people *dear*.

I shuffled closer on my knees.

'I'll ring its neck,' she whispered.

I leant back.

'What?' I said.

'You call police, I'll snap its neck like it's a hen,' she said. I stood up and stepped away from her. I couldn't help projecting fear onto the owlet watching from the nest. I couldn't help imagining it wanted its sibling back. But of course owls sometimes eat their siblings. They are not sentimental that way.

'For God's sake, just give me the chick.'

'You call the police, I'll snap it,' she said.

I stepped backwards towards the barn door. 'You little witch,' I said. 'You just dare. I'll snap your neck.'

I went back into the house and phoned the police. I was shaking.

They came out within fifteen minutes. A male and female officer. I could hardly watch as they strode through the barn door.

But the chick was all right. She had not damaged it.

Jack followed the officers into the barn with a ladder and saw that the owlet was returned to the nest.

The girl was taken away, wrapped in a tartan blanket from our bedroom. I watched from the kitchen, without the lights on. I didn't think she'd be able to see me as she got in the car, but she did seem to cast a look in my direction.

When she was gone I went back to the barn to see the two chicks in the nest. 'Right as rain,' Jack said. They both looked at me with faces like Venetian masks and I couldn't tell which one of them had been out of the nest.

The fact that the girl had been found was mentioned briefly on the regional news. The local paper ran a headline the next day, 'Our Caitlyn found safe.' No more was said of her after that, nothing in the paper, nothing on the television news.

We didn't know why she had run away, why does a girl that age not want to go home? I was left with a sense that I'd carried out a small act of betrayal. I'd called her a witch, though she was just a child. There is another superstition that owls are witches in disguise. Maybe that was at the back of my mind. Over time I've come to think I handled it as well as anyone could. I saw her once in the village, wearing the same hooded jacket though the sun was out. She did not look at me and perhaps wouldn't even have recognised me if she had. We often believe others think of us more than they do. We've got to know a few local people now. Surely we'd have heard, if there was something more to her story to hear.

So, summer came around and the owlets fledged. Another friend of Jack's, a photographer, visited and took some beautiful pictures of them in flight. We've put three enlarged black-and-white prints on the wall leading up the stairs. We're hoping the owls will have another brood this coming spring. We've rather given up on our library. I do not fear the ill omen barn owls are supposed to offer; I like to think if anything they'll bring us luck.

Ian McDonough

BANSHEE

When you were young in the 60s
the songs said 'Let it all hang out'
and 'Feelin' groovy'.
but you knew people would have scattered
if you'd let it all hang out,
and you sure weren't feeling groovy.

Growing into pain, you warmed yourself
against your wrath, nursing it
like a peat fire
on a winter morning
in that harsh and loveless croft.

Assuming your profession like a magic cloak
you husbanded yourself,
let the walls and uniform of the school
be your uniform, your walls.
And then who would know
that a banshee roamed the corridors,
choosing those most blithe and radiant
to bear the laceration of your teeth and nails?

Alan Macfarlane

SHIOGAMA DOCKS

We'd bang our heels against the harbour wall
and watch the restless headland water break,
then track the nudging trawlers' rise and fall
and guess how long each boat's approach would take.
The whaling ships might let us climb on deck
to stand beside the men who worked the crane
that dropped the fish for businessmen to check
then swept the netting back on board again.

This afternoon my son sat on the wall
to paint his latest canvas of the bay.
At ten to three he stopped and made a call
to tell me that the sea had slipped away.
I listened as he ran for higher ground
then heard the shapeless wave close in around.

Alan Macfarlane

HITTING THE TOWN

Sasha stepped onto the tram and pushed into an otherwise empty carriage. She shook the rain from her hair and moved towards the back.

'Why do people have to stand in doorways?' she said, loud enough for everyone to hear.

Ben followed on, but a muscle-bound man in an expensive-looking suit stepped across the aisle and blocked his way. He stood with his back to Ben and stared at Sasha.

'Fuckin' bitch', he said.

The man then turned, smiled down at Ben and swept some of Sasha's raindrops from his sleeve into Ben's face. Ben blinked, said nothing and squeezed by.

Sasha was now sitting in the far corner looking out at the street, both hands pushed into her pockets. Ben slid onto the seat in front and sat with his back against the window so that he could look at her, if he wanted to, or look at him, if he needed to. As Ben settled himself, the tram bell rang and the concertina doors in the middle of the carriage grated themselves shut.

'Roxy next,' said Sasha.

'Big queue,' said Ben.

'Should be,' she said.

The tram jolted itself alive then stopped momentarily before the mechanism re-caught and it began humming through the gears. Ben looked up from his wet trainers and scanned the tram. The muscle-bound man in the expensive-looking suit had stepped back into his group now, but he was still staring at them.

'I'd like to go to the Quayside later,' said Ben.

'Weather's brought them up here,' said Sasha.

'I suppose.'

'Tomorrow maybe,' she said.

The tram was already beginning to slow down when Ben lifted his forehead at Sasha, directing her to look at the street behind. The queue for the Roxy was enormous.

'Busy, busy,' he said.

'Umbrellas,' was all she said.

The tram was now almost at a halt. Sasha turned back to Ben. She put a hand on the back of his seat and made to get up, but he immediately put his hand on top of hers and pushed down.

She looked at him.

Ben rolled his eyes and nodded down the carriage. Sasha looked up and saw that the muscle-bound man in the expensive-looking suit was staring right at her. The tram doors flung open and the others in his group got off. But *he* didn't move. They were now the only people left on the tram. Sasha slipped her hand from under Ben's and sat down again.

The man grinned.

Sasha kept looking at him, but Ben sat with his head down and arms folded tight across his chest, pulling in his jacket.

Then the bell rang and the concertina started to grate together again. But the muscle-bound man in the expensive-looking suit still didn't move. He kept staring at Sasha, laughing at her as she watched the two sides getting closer and closer. Then, just as they were about to meet, he slid the toe of one of his expensive-looking shoes between the doors.

'Nearly missed my stop,' he said. 'Good job I'm standin' in the fuckin' doorway, eh?'

The muscle-bound man in the expensive-looking suit pulled the doors open and stepped down onto the pavement. Sasha watched the doors close behind him, then she and Ben sat quietly as the tram spluttered through its routine once more. As the mechanism re-took, Ben looked up and sought out the muscle-bound man on the pavement. He was still staring at them. Ben stared back.

'Well Sash?' he said.

'Just this,' she said, handing Ben a necklace. 'You?'

He reached into his pocket and pulled out a gold watch, just the kind that you might wear with an expensive-looking suit.

Rachael McGill

HORRIBLE SUNSHINE

They show the trailer again, as we're sitting down for dinner. I look away. 'Watch love go horribly wrong for six desperate dreamers!' In the background, that awful tune, 'Walking on Sunshine', a piss-take I presume. I'm knackered, don't want to fight, but we do. '*Horribly wrong*!' I shout at Coral. 'You don't get love, you get laughed at!'

She pouts. 'That's what happened to those people, might not happen to me.'

'They set it up so that's what happens. It's nasty. It'll hurt you.'

'You say that about everything.'

'This is not me being over-protective! Nobody would want their daughter to go on this. It's not a way of being famous . . .'

'I don't care about being famous! I just want . . .'

'I know, you want a boyfriend. Be patient. Maybe someone at the theatre group . . .'

'I don't fancy any of them!'

She sulks for the rest of her jacket potato, but by pudding she's clingy, wanting a story about me and her dad. They've got a different flavour now – not bedtime fairy stories, more pieces in the relationship/sex jigsaw she's putting together. She sees so much stuff on TV, sugar-coating (not that I was ever much good at it) doesn't work any more.

She asks, 'Was everyone in your theatre group having sex with each other?'

'Pretty much.'

'Not like my theatre group!'

Thank God.

She says, 'Tony said he had a girlfriend but I think he's lying. And Sebastian said he went to a prostitute.'

'What?'

I'm glad they're discussing this stuff. Natasha, the facilitator, is great, one of those relentlessly positive people who always amaze me. Doesn't mean I like to think about Coral trying to get her head round prostitution.

'But they didn't have sex. They both started crying instead.'

'Sebastian and the prostitute?'

'Yeah.'

'You see, Coral, sex can be very . . .'

'I know! So did you have sex with all the other actors?'

'No, no. Your father and I were a couple, we just didn't have a very . . . settled life.'

'You didn't have a house!'

'No.'

'You slept in the trees, like monkeys!'

'That was only once. We slept in the van.'

'And on top of the van, under the stars.'

'Yes.'

'Did you have sex on top of the van?'

'Oh, probably.'

I turn my face away. Not probably, definitely. It's still clear as day, even though I was such a different person then it's debatable I was even me, not to mention the fact I was almost certainly off my nut on something.

'Was it like walking on sunshine?' Coral asks.

I sing, 'Yeah, yeah!'

Then her rage is back, like flicking a switch. 'I want to have sex on top of a van! I want to go on the telly and walk on sunshine! Why won't you let me?!' When I try to come near her, she flings out her arm, knocks my glasses off. She's taller than me now, too strong for me to manhandle her into bed – not a delicate coral, more like an oak tree. I just have to wait for her to exhaust herself. But there's enough sadness in her to make a lot of anger.

She doesn't mention the TV programme for a few days. I hope she's forgotten. But they discuss it at the theatre group on Thursday. (Sebastian, who made the prostitute cry, is planning to apply.) When Coral gets home, she's worked up. She doesn't say much, just tells me about Sebastian, says she hates me, calls her dinner 'cabbage food', goes to bed early.

About four a.m. I hear a noise. I think foxes, or cats shagging. Then a banging, from the kitchen. It's the fridge door being opened and closed, in time with the wailing. I call to Coral, soothing things. There's no pause in the weird rhythm.

I can't get in the kitchen, she's barricaded the door with something. For the first time, I see it like words printed inside my skull: Coral could do real damage now, in one of her rages: to the house, me, herself. I lose it then, scream and swear that if she wants me to treat her like an adult, she has to behave like one. The wailing changes to crying. I sit by the door, start wittering: more stories about me and her dad, performing our trippy version of the Tempest in a lake at moonlight, to an audience of five, him getting thrown out of a church for doing his fire-eating act.

She opens the door. Her pyjamas are covered in food stains. The fridge door's hanging open. The fridge is empty apart from a few jars of pickles, half an onion and my tin of coffee.

'Where have you put the food?'

She says, using that teenage intonation she knows annoys me, 'I ate it.'

There are empty packets, vegetable remains, piled on the floor.

'All of it? A whole tub of butter? A raw aubergine?'

'I put tomato puree on it,' she said. 'It was okay.'

'Why?'

'I was hungry.'

She's the picture of desolation, so I can't laugh. I'm too horrified anyway. I shock myself by not wanting to hug her: she towers above me, a snot-encrusted, tomato puree-smeared monster.

'What's this about?' My voice shakes. Please, not eating disorders.

She ignores my question, says, 'Tell me about the drugs.'

I wish I never had. I was trying to answer her big question, the one that plagues her. All I managed to do was give her someone to blame, the person it hurts her most to blame: me. Maybe I've been over-compensating in the other direction since that slip up. I loathe myself for it more than any of the other things I loathe myself for. Coral knows that. She makes me tell her again whenever she's angry.

I say, 'Your dad was a person who liked to try things out, even dangerous things. He kept looking for his perfect drug.'

'You did too!' she roars in my face.

'And I . . . took things with him, till I realised I was pregnant.'

'Which wasn't for a long time, because you were . . . stupid or something.'

'Because I . . . my periods were never regular, sometimes they stopped altogether . . .'

'Because of the drugs!'

'Maybe. More likely because I didn't eat very well.'

'Why not?'

'I was young, I had no money, and . . .'

She fixes me with her need-to-know-now look. Before I realise it, I've offered another old truth: 'and I thought I was fat. I always wanted to be thinner.'

'You? Fat?' she spat at me. 'I'm the fat one!'

'You're not fat.' She's not really, just large, a person on a different scale from me. And, unlike me, she's got great breasts. Another thing to worry about.

'I am. It's your fault. You made me fat!'

'No, no.'

'We're all a bit fat, at the theatre group. Fatter than normal people. It's part of it. Don't tell me it's not.'

I whisper, 'I don't know.' It's hard to catch my breath.

'Because of your drugs I'm learning disabled and fat and I can never have a normal life, I don't get walking on sunshine, I get horribly wrong, and I always have to be treated like a child, and I hate it! You don't know how awful it is to be me!'

She's right. I only know how awful it is to be myself.

*

The director, Liam, invites me to meet him at his house. Which is so weird, I almost don't go. But when I get to the place – the ground floor of a Georgian terrace in an area that gentrified before the word existed – and see bookshelves and hangings from his travels and whatnot through the window, I understand why he's done it: to lay himself bare, so I trust him. I can't decide if it's what a twat would do.

Coral kept saying, when she begged me to talk to him, that Liam was 'REALLY nice' when he came to the theatre group. She went a bit coy, as if she might be confusing finding a boyfriend through the programme with going out with him. I don't know if Coral looks at adult men and fancies them, or just likes the concept of 'boyfriend'. Whenever I wonder about that, I stop myself going there.

He comes to the door. I think course she fancies him, who the hell wouldn't, shit. He's tall and honed, he's got straggly curly hair that he has no right to have at his age, a twinkly smile and . . . not good. I hate him for enchanting my daughter. At the same time, a bit of me is wondering if he'll try to do the same to me.

He doesn't. He seems almost shy. He makes tea, apologises for the biscuits – Penguins, but not the green ones because his son likes those. Then he apologises, for about twenty minutes, for the marketing of the programme. He says he was incensed, it wasn't what he wanted, it's not what the programme's like. The programme is 'sensitive,' raises important issues about social perceptions of learning disability, and not everything goes wrong for everyone.

I try not to snort. 'Some people find love, do they?'

'Yes,' he says. 'Some of them did.' He actually gets choked up. 'That's the main reason we want to do another series.'

'Not cause of the great ratings you'll get by giving people a freak show?'

He doesn't get defensive, just waits for me to get it off my chest, then says 'Do you want to see?'

We watch an extract – a boy called Martin, with a mild learning disability, who looks like a teenager, but is probably in his early twenties, like Coral, meeting a Down's Syndrome girl called Tessa. It touches some nerves. Martin talks about how hard it is having no private life. He says, 'I can never make mistakes, not even tiny ones. Normal people are allowed to make mistakes.' I cringe at his use of the word 'normal' – what Coral says too, despite all my attempts not to present it that way. Martin makes tons of mistakes on his dates with Tessa. He plays to the camera a little. They both laugh their heads off about it. I've got tears streaming down my cheeks, not the laughter kind. So does Liam, though he must've seen it God knows how many times. The interviewer asks them about sex: they haven't had it yet. Tessa says, 'The first time I had sex was with a friend of my sister's. He told me I should, so I did, but it wasn't very nice. Then I had a boyfriend for a few weeks, but whenever we had sex I felt frightened. I liked it better when we just held hands, or went to the cinema.' It's Coral all over. It gives me a physical longing to run home and hug her.

It is done carefully, compassionately. It's more documentary than reality show. But I'm not amused with Liam for making me bawl in front of him. When he switches it off, I don't compliment him. I babble, 'They're so . . . it's not . . . it shouldn't be television.'

'You don't think people should understand better how it is for them?' he says.

I know it's selfish. I say it anyway. 'Not through my daughter.'

'I understand,' he says. 'I felt that way too, but it was Martin who had the idea for the programme, persuaded me to pitch it.'

'That Martin?' I gesture at the screen.

'Yes,' says Liam. 'My son.'

I do a double take or three.

'You could meet him, ask him about it yourself,' says Liam, 'if you wanted to stick around for half an hour.' He looks away, flushes. Some very rusty cogs inside my brain start to work. They tell me he's shy about the fact he wants me to stay for another half hour. I flush too.

'Where is he?' I ask.

'Playing football with friends. He'll be back for *Home and Away*.'

'Who's . . . looking after him?'

'The other boys. I trust them.'

'It's different with girls,' I say. 'I could never let Coral go out with a group of other young people, no adults around. When she started going to the sex education project, the theatre thing, I went online for stuff about how to talk to her about sex. There was story after story of abuse. It seems normal for those girls to get abused by someone at some point. Like Tessa.'

'My future daughter-in-law,' Liam says. 'They want to get married, get a place of their own.' He gives a little laugh. 'I don't know if they could handle it. But the social workers say maybe they can, and I have to let them try. That's scary.'

'Are you . . .?' I want to say 'on your own', but that sounds like flirting. He reads me.

'It's just been me and Martin for the last ten years,' he says.

Our eyes meet for too long. I say, 'Well, it'd be nice to see him. I could stay for a bit, if I could get another Penguin.'

*

I'm still a bit high when I get home. (I'm walking on sunshine, yeah, yeah. Just a small raylet.) I pretend to myself it's cause I'm excited about telling Coral she can apply for the programme, if she's sure that's what she wants. As soon as I see her, the clouds come over. She's curled up on the sofa, hugging a cushion. She looks like she's been crying.

'Did something happen?' I ask.

She shrugs. She's learned how to not tell me (and anyone else who'll listen) every thought that passes through her mind. I should be pleased she's maturing, but I'd got used to having a child I could see the internal workings of. If I wait, she might talk later. Or maybe – this is harder to handle – she won't, cause it's something she hasn't understood herself.

'You're right,' I say. 'Liam is very nice. I decided that if you really want to, you can apply for the programme.'

She looks up, frowns, searches my face.

'You look different,' she says.

I do a silly, nervous laugh. Different like a woman who just flirted with a bloke for the first time in two decades? Coral wouldn't see that, would she?

'Different how?'

'Pretty, or something.'

'Ha,' I said, 'that is different!'

She rolls her eyes. 'I didn't mean you're not always pretty, Mum, for God's sake. Why are you always so . . .?' She can't remember the word, gives herself a tap on the side of the head, punishing the brain that lets her down.

'Negative? Cynical? Filled with self-loathing?' I suggest, bombarding her with too many words. Cruel. Impatient. A bad mother.

'I don't want to do the show any more,' Coral says.

'Okay,' I say. 'Why not?'

'I don't want horrible sunshine. If I can't have real sunshine, like normal people, it's better not to try.'

'Real sunshine is for everyone, Coral.' It comes out even less convincing than it sounds in my head.

We go into the kitchen. I try again to teach Coral to make an omelette. She'll get there, if we repeat it over and over. It's easier when she's not in a chatty mood: I don't have to keep shouting 'focus!'

I do the onion. She slices a courgette, painstakingly, her sad face and her concentrating face merging into an expression that makes me desperate. Finally she says, almost whispers, 'I'm not ready to have sex.'

I pause, half way to the frying pan with the chopped onion, say 'That's fine Coral. Is it anything in particular, that made you decide . . .?'

'My thighs,' she mumbles.

'What?'

'A woman's thighs are not supposed to touch in the middle, but mine do. Not just touch . . . they . . . they . . .' Her breathing gets shallow. I put a hand on her arm, say, 'It's okay, slow down.'

'They squidge,' she finishes. 'So I have to learn to do exercise or something, and if that doesn't work I have to save up to get them . . . fixed, before anyone will ever . . . you have to take all your clothes off, don't you?'

I swallow my fury, put the chopping board down, hug her, tell her she doesn't have to do anything, there is no way thighs are 'supposed' to be, the world is full of people talking shit about bodies and sex, she has to ignore it. This is a hard concept for Coral, whose life is mostly about navigating rules.

'I think I might not ever be ready to have sex,' says Coral.

'That's okay!'

'It's not,' she says. 'I don't want to be a weirdo.'

I tell her she's not weird, she's wonderful, I'll always look after her, she doesn't have to feel she has to rush to do grown up (I don't say 'normal') things. We agree it wouldn't be a good idea for her to do the show. We're together, safe. A little door closes on my raylet of light. I don't mind. That would've ended up horrible sunshine too.

I beat the eggs. She passes me a plate of cheese she's grated. She says, 'You know, Mum, just cause I'm not doing the programme, doesn't mean you can't see him again.'

My fingers fail to grip. The plate falls to the floor and shatters, ribbons of cheese attach themselves to my ankle. Coral shouts, 'Focus!'

James McGonigal

HEARING AID (NOISY BASTARDS)

Stop shouting at me, everything!
Cold-tap NIAGARA roaring into the sink.
Knife across a slice of toast SANDPAPERING
my skull. Just a scratch at the leg of my jeans is
CRAMPONS along an icy ridge. I can hear you,
shoelaces HISSING like a noose and you,
moist BLADE pirouetting on this page's wintry lake.

No wonder the house-mice shrink from us, miners
in great PIT BOOTS along the upper gallery,
howking out the nuggets of our day.
Would you listen to what they're squeaking:

**NOISY BASTARDS. CAN YOU NOT THROW US
ONE CRUMB OF PEACE?**

Roddie McKenzie

THE SNOWS OF BEN NEVIS

The light is going as we near the top of the ridge. I click on my head torch. The Tower Gap to cross next and then the summit. It's like being in a plane: the Carn Mor Dearg arête below, covered in soft white, Loch Linnhe a silver finger intermittently pointing south-west, as the fleeting clouds smoke by in the rising wind. It hits us without warning. One moment I am sticking my axes into the ice like hammering nails into a wall in the whistling spindrift, next thing there is a crack like a shotgun immediately above me and the slope avalanches onto me.

I'm upside down, tumbling, like being in a washing machine, but at the temperature of a kitchen freezer. There is a colossal jerk on the rope that links me to Chris on his belay ledge below. More tumbling, pain from collisions with hard things, the blood seeping into my clothes. And then . . . blackness.

I open my eyes in what could be my grave. It's white, blue and crystalline in the light of my torch. The panic screams in my head, my chest is bursting. Can't breathe! Can't breathe! I'm choking on icy debris, but I vomit and it passes, it's so cold I can't smell the orange muck freezing on the chest of my down jacket. What was it that Billy Connolly said? Puke looks like boiled carrots, so don't eat boiled carrots and you'll never hurl.

Where the fuck did that come from?

I spit out the snow. It goes away from my face to my neck, so I must be pointed upward. Have I been out for a while? The cold snow grates on my exposed face and calves. The pressure tightens. The debris is beginning to freeze, to solidify, trapping me like thae fossil fish embedded in a layer of sandstone, that I remember seeing as a kid in the Art Galleries at Kelvingrove.

Suddenly that will to live lunges forward like a motorbike going into gear. I feel the acceleration – everything is on fast forward. I'm able to free one hand from the freezing cement and push it from my face, but I lose a mitt in the process. As I scrape above my face, it seems like forever, but after many rests, I get my face clear of the rock – hard crust. I'm lucky – I'm not in too deep. The bitter wind swirls around me, abrasive as the sanding disc that I use in the yard. Before long I can't feel my nose and chin and, more ominously, the fingers of my ungloved hand. But the worst is the feeling in my legs, of being buried in a giant slushy, composed of setting concrete that chills all the way through the layers of clothing. Remember as a kid, when you made too many snowballs without gloves and your hands burned – the agony? But gradually, all the feeling went away, just like now.

I still have one axe. With the point, I hack away at the setting white mass over my legs – a couple of shots rebound off of bone, but thank God for the cold because I don't feel it. The slices don't hurt but the sticky blood clots almost as soon as I touch it. Pain doesn't register over the rush of adrenalin. The panic over, I know I can do this now. Fuck it! I'm Tony McKellern, Scotland's Hot Rock freestyle champion of 2010. It takes a long time, in between agonising gasps of the bitter air, but now I'm out of the slide debris. And then the shivers start. It's all a bit spacey.

I can't see the stars. They must be starting to come out up there, somewhere, but everything is grey. Jeez, it's so, so cold, even through this expensive gear. But as I push myself up on my hands, I lean on something smooth. In the beam of my helmet torch, through the white swirl, I recognise the orange cupola of another helmet. It must be Chris. I scrape down. It takes a long time, bracing and stumbling against the screaming wind. Eventually I can pull him over and clear the snow from his face. His flesh is pale blue. I slap him hard with my numb hand; he moves under the blow and recoils.

'Chris buddy, it's going to be okay – we're out of the slide, I'm calling mountain rescue – we'll be okay mate – we'll make it – just fuckin' hang in there.' He's looking down and is crying.

'Fuck, Chris, talk to me – that's better – hey pal, we're mates! No I'm not gonna leave you – look we're getting out of this together. Yeah, shake on that, you got it.'

'What's that – you want me to call Tina? Sure mate, no probs – Look, I'm going to put a call in for help and fire the flares – hey, we'll be home and drinking whisky before you know it.'

'What? Yeah don't worry pal – I'm doing it. Shit you're a worrier!'

I turn away from him and, after an eternity of fumbling, pull the flare from the top pocket of my rucksack. I light it and it shoots upward into the blizzard and bursts crimson, in a pattern like on thae rhubarb desserts they used to serve us in primary school.

'Hey Chris, you remember yon rhubarb desserts at school, in the fancy glasses – posh eh? Fur coat and nae knickers we used to call them – like nae ice cream or custard underneath – just stewed rhubarb and a wee tate o' cream. Mind?'

I think he laughs, or maybe it's his injured face and him trying to breathe. He doesn't look up. So I have to commentate for him.

'Hey will you look at these colours, Chris? Pretty magic with that snow and the wind and all – know whit ah mean? You're no very talkative – anyway – you're staying awake – that's the main thing in survival eh? Give me a nod, if you want something . . . won't be long now'. He opens his eyes. His eyebrows are frosted, he looks like an old man, grey, white-haired.

'What, you want some Glenlivet? No sorry – no can do mate, you know it chills you faster, c'mon mate – you know that.'

He's always been an obstreperous bugger, but he's not getting any. It takes another eternity of fumbling, but I get my phone out – still got bars – that's good. I hit the keypads with the fingers of my good hand. I have to yell in his ear over the wind.

'Look calm down, I'm phoning them – look got a signal – sorry Chris, shut up for a sec mate – I gotta tell rescue where we are.'

'Yeah injuries, possible broken legs – we need heli-vac.'

'Yeah, Chris – I've told them the story – they're coming to get us – no worries mate, stay cool.'

'What Tina? Yeah. Huuhhh . . .? Okay. Look give me a minute – you're a carnaptious bugger for a casualty. Gie's a break! I'll call her in a sec – sit tight and wait for the RAF boys.'

The phone rings out – wow that was fast. I look at Chris and put a shushing finger to my numb lips. They are coming. Someone must have seen the flare right enough.

'Yeah! Yes – I can hear you – you've seen the flare – awesome man! Don't worry we urnae going anywhere. Hey – Thanks man!'

'Chris – they've seen us, RAF say they saw the flare! Hang in there man.' He smiles but I can tell he's hurting bad.

'What? You're cold? Look have my jacket, I'm not too bad now – yeah there you go. That's better, eh?' He's clearly in pain but smiles. The darkness is total now.

'Don't worry, they'll be there soon – just keep talking to me – c'mon we got to look after each other – we'll keep each other awake. Yeah – that's true, know what you mean – fuckit – don't sleep – what was that now Chris?'

*

'Foxtrot Alpha to Lossiemouth Control . . . dawn coming up away to the east . . . Still no contact from the missing party? Please confirm, over.'

'Lossiemouth Control to Foxtrot Alpha, negative Foxtrot Alpha, nothing since they were reported overdue last night.'

'Foxtrot Alpha, roger Control, over'.

'Foxtrot Alpha to Control, I'm seeing avalanche debris on summit of the Little Tower . . . coming up on it now, Great Tower looks okay . . . seeing no tracks rising onto the Tower gap or exit ramps . . . over.'

'Control to Alpha, I understand, the casualties must be on the Little Tower, over.'

'Alpha to Lossiemouth Control . . . winchman reporting a casualty below Great Tower, garment flapping in the breeze caught his eye. Under the Great Tower now . . . switching to thermal imaging, one heat source, repeat one thermal. I have on visual now. I can confirm one casualty, one casualty only . . . over.'

'Lossiemouth Control, understood Foxtrot Alpha, one survivor.'

'Foxtrot Alpha to Lossiemouth Control, preparing to deploy winch man for casualty evac, over.'

*

'Shit, almost dropped off there, Chris.' I wake as my head nods forward. The wind is roaring, snow swirls around me up into the darkness but the moon must be up, it's lighting up the flurries. It's huge, filling my vision, it's dazzling. The snow is spiralling upward, it's so beautiful, a tornado of stars. In the glare I see a silhouetted figure descending slowly toward me. It is gesturing with its hands, I can't see a face – it's one big gleam of light. It must be an angel . . . it's coming for me. I've not made it, it's over. For some reason, I'm not bothered, I gave it a good shot . . . now, I can sleep.

I open my eyes. Gradually, I make sense of the image: a guy in a flying helmet is leaning over me. I realise that the thundering is the helicopter engine, there is no wind, but the weather is flying by the window. I'm in a sleeping bag, but the shivering won't stop. The horror strikes and I struggle to sit up.

'Chris? CHRIS!' He gently pushes me back down.

'Okay Tony mate, easy now, you're going to hospital, you'll be okay, good job we found you when we did.'

'But we got to go back, I'm all right, Chris is the one that needs your help, we got to go and get him.' His face softens, he reaches over and picks up a broken yellow helmet from the floor behind me.

'Was this Chris's? I couldn't get it out of your hands when we winched you up.'

Hugh McMillan

ACCOUNTING FOR ELSPETH MCQUEEN, KIRKCUDBRIGHT 1689

3 pounds for peat
16 shillings for coal
4 for rope, 4 for a tar barrel
8 for a drum beat.

The stink came free.
The smoke curled
in clouds above the Tolbooth,
cut off the light all day.

The minister
said his horse sweated blood
when they brought her in,
that she spoiled

her neighbours' milk.
Guid folk all,
few there that day
beyond the executioner

who cost the council,
they noted, a pint at the start,
seven more
while she burned.

David McVey

MY MEMORIES OF SEAL CLUBBING

I always enjoyed seal clubbing. On Orkney, where I grew up, it was the highlight of the year and everyone looked forward to it. And the seals? They were all in favour of it. They *wanted* us to come.

Of course, when I say 'the seals' I really mean the seal folk, those we called the *selkies*. In real life they're very different from the melancholy, sinister creatures of legend, who look mournfully at the human world on which they've turned their backs and who maybe rise from the water now and again to take a human lass as a wife. In fact, many seal-folk, male and female, live a double life, living in the sea but often returning to Orkney, to the land; they like, now and again, to feel the solidity of the earth beneath their pelts, to meet up with old friends, to switch from their sea-food to potatoes and beef and bread. 'Sand eels!' one of my seal-folk friends once said to me. 'Can you imagine what it's like to live on nothing but *sand eels*?'

And of course, in June, as Midsummer approached, they thought only of dancing, of shaking the sea and the salt from their pelts, resuming human form, and going clubbing.

The seventies were the glory days of seal clubbing, or *selkie disco* as we called it then. A field would be roped off and a massive sound system delivered there. Food caravans appeared, toilet units were installed in regimented lines; and then the selkies came.

Black bullet heads in their hundreds appeared in the bays and voes in what was more of a migration than a mere arrival. They hauled themselves onto the beaches in massive numbers, shed their pelts and walked as humans towards the venue, thronging the roads and paths. This would usually be on the Wednesday or Thursday nearest to Midsummer, and the music would start to soar and resound over the hills and moors and fields and out to sea where the shyer selkies would perhaps turn their whiskered noses towards the island-clamour and wonder whether they too should have headed for the land.

As the weekend approached, young human folk would turn from their work in field or workshop. The bars and hotels would be empty as the island young folk avoided them and sought out instead the disco field and met with the selkies and gave themselves over to the music. We called it 'disco' but rock was the music of choice, especially the faster, louder tracks from *Led Zeppelin 4*, *Who's Next*, *Deep Purple in Rock* and Free's *Fire and Water*. Somewhere between beach and field the selkies would put on some human clothes and join up with old friends and acquire some bottles and cans so that they could begin the process of getting seriously hammered.

As I've said, selkies are far from the ethereal, wistful creatures of sea-myth and story; many never turned their backs fully on the human world. Some retained homes and bank accounts on Orkney and would work ashore for lengthy periods on farms, in shops or in factories in Stromness and Kirkwall. Sam Yorston was a returning selkie I'd been at school with. I remember sitting with him on the fringe of the dancing one Midsummer in a field near Stenness, swigging occasionally from bottles of beer. 'It's all very well,' he said, 'the idyllic life swimming free in the deep green wrack-swirl, but some of us like to come back here to drink and eat hearty food and enjoy some *comfort*.'

Drink did for a lot of selkies, though; get incapacitated too often and they'd lose the ability to slew off the human form and its limitations, to take back their pelts and slip back into the silky ocean and resume life as one of the sleek, streamlined animals we knew so well. Often, as the moon rose over a dance-field that rippled with a solid mass of gyrating figures, Sam would point out one staggering, swaying sealman in human form, barely conscious with the amount of lager he'd necked, and say, 'That one will be landbound soon.' And he was always right. The individual would long to return to the water, to swim again with the seal-lasses and explore the green-lit depths, but would no longer be able to. He would remain a sad, drunken, very human wretch. Few lived long; many were found drowned on the water's edge.

The dances were always strange scenes. The selkies welcomed us land folk, as I've said, and many of them had resumed full human form and were indistinguishable from us. But a few had retained some parts of seal anatomy. For some it was the doleful, sad-eyed bullet-head, but for far more it was the fore-flippers, which they claimed were ideal for throwing cool new moves on the dancefloor. These selkies rarely drank much (you can't hold a can or bottle with flippers) and always safely returned to the sea.

I left Orkney in the autumn of 1979. I remember my last seal clubbing session, on a sultry night in June when many seal-folk retained their pelts the better to protect against the midges. By then it was The Clash and The Jam and The Police that we favoured and the music thudded out into the dark spaces of a Midsummer night. In later years, I understand, tourists from the south began to find out about seal clubbing and came to share the experience, to watch and learn, and sometimes to dance.

By the early 1990s, the music had deteriorated and the young seal-folk gyrated repetitively to sterile electronic dance beats, alien and alienating. Many were blissing themselves into a permanent land-life with a mixture of e tablets and cheap lager from the island supermarkets.

By then there were even more visitors from the south, and some of them pondered deeply about the field-dancing, the atmosphere and the magical coinciding of fresh open air and thumping music. Suppose, they thought, we take all this, and replace the recorded music with live bands and artists? And so they returned south to organise the massive resurgence of outdoor festivals in the late 1990s and early 2000s.

By the new millennium, the seal clubbing scene was dead. Young Orkney folk travelled to T in the Park and Glastonbury instead, and the number of returning selkies dwindled. Too many were landbound, now. The last event happened in 1999, a pitiable affair aimed at Elvis impersonators among the selkie community. After the last slow dance, the music of 'I Can't Help Falling in Love' faded into the brackish Orkney air; I'm told the whistling of sea-selkies could then be heard out in the Pentland Firth. The dancers threw off their quiffs and sideburns and shades, slipped into their pelts and took to the water. Many never returned.

Of course, some of them do still come back to Orkney; they might attend church on Communion Sundays, visit their families at Christmas and Hogmanay or book into hotels for a few days to enjoy some proper food. They still sometimes work onshore during the summer, meet up with old friends, take part in community events but *you don't really notice them*. They look just like us and they make sure that they don't stand out. I haven't visited Orkney in June for many years but I'm told Midsummers are quiet affairs, now, except for the daft hippies from the south who chant nonsense at the Neolithic sites.

But somewhere, still, beneath the sky and the waves, the sea-selkies swim on in a green world of silence.

Laura Morgan

ON AN EARTH UNIFORMLY COVERED BY SEA

The roof had already been knocked, leaving just four walls and a crumbling concrete floor. Callum stared at the hardheads growing in his uncle's yard. The whole reason for his trip north was for a bit of peace to study, and yet here he was, a quick visit with Uisdean turning into a 'wee job'.

'So what do you think?' his uncle asked.

'How long will take?'

'Day or two for the frame, another couple for the sheets.'

A breeze stirred up the smell of old straw. Callum's resit was only a fortnight away, but then he did study best late at night.

'I'll no be doing evenings mind. I've this exam, like.'

Uisdean said that was fine and, after they'd shaken on it, Callum walked back to his mam's. In his room he set about unpacking. He'd been too tired the night before, taking out only his toothbrush. Now he pulled the books one by one from his bag and stacked them on the windowsill. The set text, the others from the reading list, the course handout and the two A4 pads of his own scrawled jottings. He opened the cover of *Foundations of Fluid Dynamics* and let his eyes flit over the contents, the layering of chapters and subtitles – the light from his small window warmer somehow and thicker than the light that washed from the tall windows of the refectory. He dropped the book on top of the others and watched the dust in the room surge and swirl in something like the movement of the sea. He felt that easy wash inside himself. He could give the revising a miss for one night surely.

His mam gave him a shake early the next morning. It was like old times, his hurrying down to Uisdean's to cadge a day's work. Together they lifted the tarp off the pile of timber behind the byre. Callum's first job was to take a broom to the lengths, sweeping them free of the stoor that had gathered there from the damp and winds of the two winters they'd lain under cover – nothing ever got done in

a hurry up here. Along with the yard dirt, the wood had become a
home for sleeping moths. Wings folded, they hid themselves in holes
in the pile like splinters of a darker wood. They were reluctant to
wake and, with the sun in his eyes, he brushed at them impatiently.

'I'd forgotten about the moths,' he said.

'Hang on till I get another count on these rafters. Six, eight, ten.
You should have two more there and then the joists. You thought
any more on that job?'

Uisdean had an old bosun pal in Newcastle who might take Callum
as a trainee. Marine engineering. Propellers, shafting systems.

Callum shrugged. 'I'm halfway through uni now.'

'It's not often Donald takes trainees.'

'But Newcastle. I don't know. They're supposed to be taking on a
load of folk up here soon. With the decommissioning, like.'

'You want to be looking to the future, no be coming back for a
job that's temporary.'

It was all you heard from the time you were wee. Dounreay's
closing, nothing to take its place, get a degree and get out, there's
no money in sheep. His mam had stood over him while he signed
the uni applications. 'Don't be going to Aberdeen,' she'd said. 'It's
too close. You want to, you know . . . spread your wings.'

They made the most of the fine weather and by eight that night
they'd got the rafters measured and each joint cut and tested. Uisdean
said that was enough for one day. Callum grabbed his hoody from
the grass and headed off over the fields.

The days passed with him balancing on the byre walls, fixing the
frame in place, the headland dropping away beneath him – a feeling
of being there in the sky. Looking out the window of the fourth floor
tenement in Leith, you got that sense of height over the rooftops,
but it was different from seeing only fields and sea. Every morning
when he woke he thought about his studying, but every night he
was too tired. He'd go to bed with the tingle of sun on his skin and
a heaviness in his arms, a sudden tightening of his muscles when
he turned over. And then it would be morning again and he'd walk
over to his uncle's with the sea in the bay glowing whiter than the

sky and just a hint of dark where the lines of swell were, like a whiteboard scrubbed of its dry marker squiggles.

Some days his auntie gave him his dinner and then he and Uisdean would go out again in the evening with a breeze rushing through the long grass, and work until late, the moon crisp and white, and the sky with that pale nothingness that comes with midsummer. And then the moths would appear. One night Callum watched as their shadows clogged the dusk.

'Yellow Underwings,' his uncle said.

'*Underwings.*'

'That or Common Rustics. I've a book somewhere. Come on and put that saw away and we'll call it a night.'

When the byre's roof beams were done, he had a few days off while his uncle waited for the corrugated sheeting to be delivered. Box Profile 34/1000 with two glass fibre roof lights. Callum helped his mam around the croft. There were three lambs she'd had to hand rear and they were still getting a bottle in the evenings, their little mouths pulling at his aching arm. At bedtime, when he went to usher the hens into the coop, he watched tiny white moths in the long grass, their blank wings fluttering doggedly.

'Uisdean was just here,' his mam said, when he went inside. 'Says that's the roof stuff arrived and he'll see you in the morning.'

On his way to bed, Callum picked the top textbook from the pile on the windowsill. He could do an hour. At least get a study plan in place. He got into bed before he noticed the grey-green of the ancient fabric cover, its loose spine. *Moths of Northern Sutherland.* Uisdean must have left it. He opened the cover to black-and-white photographs, the ink too dark, and careful sketches – the powdery look of the wings captured in the stippling of the pencil. *Following eclosion from the chrysalis, the animal's veins are pumped with a blood-like fluid, and with this forceful action the wings swell to their adult shape.* It sounded painful, like a man dislocating his shoulders to fit through a hole. He fell asleep to dense dreams – prehistoric, lichen-mottled and crumbly – and then the sea rushed in and he woke to the refracting of light from its surface. But it was just the sun flashing over the dark stack of textbooks. He'd forgotten to draw his curtains.

That morning they began the sheeting out. He was halfway through his last week now, but he only really needed three days to cram, and he had the whole of the train journey too. Uisdean balanced the sheets on the roof frame and Callum hauled them up. It was hard on your back and arms and after he'd screwed in the first two his hand had a warm buzz about it. His uncle went to fetch more screws and Callum rolled his shoulders and stood to take in the view. The tide was way out, coming in on long low waves, the sun catching each breaking face so that the bay was a glitter of broken lines. Something spooked the gulls on the beach and they took off all at once into the incoming waves, suddenly swooping up and out as one broke beneath them, and scattering like scraps of paper thrown on the wind.

The last day was a long one, working late to get all the sheets in place. By now they'd struck a rhythm and Callum's arms told him when to take the weight and when to haul, his eyes seeing only ridges and runnels sliding by. About nine, he turned to take the next one and found it wasn't there.

'What's up? It's no dark yet, I can still see.'

'No for long you won't. Squall's coming.'

Sure enough a billowing grey curtain moved over the sea.

'But we've still two sheets.'

'Come on I'll get you home.'

Callum looked at the curtain coming closer. The change in light more sensed than real, though it would be with them in minutes. They should have got it finished – the tools put away and a final appraisal of their work. Uisdean started up the van just as the first drops began to fall. In the cab, with rain drumming out the engine noise, Callum thanked him for the book.

'It's very old. My great-uncle's, I think.'

'It says when they hatch first, they have to hang upside down until this blood stuff, *haemo*something, floods their wings.'

Uisdean took a hand from the wheel and gestured north to the sea and the horizon. 'I'll tell you something I remember. Being out there one night in a creel boat and looking up, and there was a moth fluttering about the cabin lamp. Five miles out we were.'

'You think it had flown there?'

'Ach, it was probably just a stowaway, but it didn't seem to know any different. Spent the whole night fluttering at that lamp.'

Callum gave the van door a farewell thump as Uisdean pulled off. It was late now, and after he peeled off his wet hoody he went to say goodnight to his mam.

'What day's this reset of yours?'

'Tuesday.'

'You haven't been doing much with the books.'

'I've two days still. Two days is fine.'

'You know, maybe you should be thinking about Australia.'

'Australia?'

'They're always needing engineers in Australia.'

'Aye,' Callum said. 'Maybe.'

He turned from her into the dark hall. His bedside light showed under the end door and he went towards its glow.

*

On Tuesday he filed into the hall with the others, left his bag at the back and carried his pencil case to the table. They sat in stuffy silence watching the clock. Beside him, an invigilator nudged a window up and fresh air drifted down.

'You may begin.'

Callum turned over the paper and read the first question. 'On an Earth uniformly covered by sea . . .' Tide theory. He reached for a pen but on opening the case found a tiny blue moth inside – inert on his ruler. He saw in its wings the sky above Strathy Bay, the shining sea, felt the roof sheets in his hands and the memory of the long, hard haul in his muscles. He thought of moths hanging upside down before taking flight – the painful swelling of their wings. Never taught a thing, only listening to their bodies.

In the draft from the tall window he sensed the city's towers and steeples, felt the breeze lifting him over the outlying towns, the network of roads, and bringing him north, further north till the traffic shrank back and the moor began, the air rippling the lochans and a dreamlike floating as grasses and reeds whipped by.

On an Earth uniformly covered by sea.

Mairi Murphy

YOUR VERSION

Jumped-up nyaff, you know nothing
of my father, with your disdainful talk:
peripheral vascular disease
a lifetime product of smoking
directed at the computer screen
even though you know he is almost deaf,
refuse to face him, man to man.
You know nothing of the boy
who was sent to Egypt on National Service
clutching a tin of cigarettes issued by the government:
his first John Player inhaled on the way over
with fear, homesickness and a lifetime addiction,
his hearing shot from the rattle of the guns.
What do you know? Piddling, meddling podiatrist
telling Dad there is no fix – he is to blame, *smoking – you see?*
Pointing out the black bits, foot and lung, what's to be done
that humiliation won't cure, certainly make worse.
And with your history, Tommy . . . aneurysm,
too dangerous to operate . . . never heal,
wounds suppurate . . . what do you expect?
What do you know, of my father? What do you know?
Twenty years of not smoking, given up after my mother's
            cancer,
his heart attack, so strong it would have killed a lesser man,
caring for us, working, guiding, loving, providing
strength and advice. A bear of a man, always on hand, wit
            and music.
Newmarket pennies to place our bets, lifting us
with one hand in feats of strength.
Show him anything
discuss everything
around our table: Communism, Catholicism,

his daily communicant father
blacklisted on the Red Clyde.
What do you know, little man, of what he can handle?
How much we need him to go on, to continue
to protect him now, fierce, as he did us.
After your consultation, he clutches the wall, doesn't want
            to go on.
How dare you judge.
How dare you, little man.

Andrew Neilson

STEVENSON'S EDINBURGH

'this dream in masonry and living rock'

Robert Louis Stevenson,
the author in his jimjams,
wrote about the New Town,
its draughty parallelograms

(the parks, squares and avenues
in which RLS grew up,
the Georgian grasp on the New
that ever shall erupt),

decrying what he saw,
the Enlightenment's modernity,
our man reserved his awe
for the Old Town's identity:

the wynds and black, volcanic rock;
the tenements, their ghosts;
Burke and Hare, the mortuary block;
the Covenanters' host.

In doing so, dear Stevenson
was sticking with the plan:
Romance over reason,
the monster over the man,

and building up the Scottish pash
for what we call duality,
that what is flame will soon be ash,
odd thoughts about mortality,

the Otherness that brands us;
we are the Otherhood,
haunted by the unconscious,
with a tendency to brood.

He was a storyteller,
the finest of the lot.
But he was another fella
who helped fuck up the Scots.

Niall O'Gallagher

'CHA TÈID AN GAOL A ROINN . . .'

Cha tèid an gaol a roinn
mar uairean oidhch' gun tàmh,
no mìosan beannaicht' cràdh
do mhàthair 's tu na broinn.

Nighean nam mile gàir'
cha tèid an gràdh na bhloigh,
na chriomag bhochd nach toigh
– cha dèan an gaol ach fàs.

Fàsaidh mar a dh'fhàsas tu
is fàsaidh m' onfhadh nam chom,
mo chridhe lom a' tàladh dhut

's mi a' tarraing analach
agus ga sèideadh air tonn
nam fonn uile a chanadh leam.

Catherine Ogston

THE STRANGER

The heap of wet clothes lay on the beach like a present from the sea. As we approached we could see the bulk of a person: a man, half dead and tangled with seaweed, like garlands from the waves.

We staggered up the path, the man's arms slung over our shoulders. I took most of the weight as Grandma was tiny and as frail as a bird against his large frame. He lurched clumsily on his feet, his head lolling as if it were loose on its fittings. In the cottage, we laid him in the bed by the fire, covered him with blankets and sent a prayer above. We were alone on the island so prayers were all we had.

When we rose the next morning the stranger sat by the hearth and watched us silently as we made tea and porridge. Grandma kept pulling her shawl around herself and casting sideways glances. I wondered when he spoke which language he would utter. At last Grandma threw her arms and fingers around, her signs and symbols painting themselves in the air.

'I will not ask him that,' I said.

She gestured at me again and from the corner of my eye I could see the stranger observing us.

'No,' I repeated and poured tea from the old pot.

'Wha' does she want to ken?' came his voice, unexpected and clear.

I sighed. 'She wants to ken if ye are a selkie.'

He looked straight at her. 'I'm no selkie,' he said and turned back to stare into the peat fire, while Grandma sipped her tea and mumbled silently.

*

The stranger stayed as there was nowhere else for him to go. He said thank you for the food we gave him and by the third day he began to wash pots and feed the hens. He rolled up his sleeves and his arms were ghostly pale, like he had never seen sunlight. His eyes were dark though, like spots of indigo ink, and I couldn't look him in the face for long before I had to turn away.

Grandma continued to ask him questions, signing to me and waiting for me to translate for her. *Where have ye come from? Who is yer father? Were ye on a ship?* He told us the name of somewhere we had never heard of; he didn't know who his father was; yes, he had been on a ship.

Grandma nodded and turned away. She had one husband and two sons lying on the seabed, melting into the saltwater, floating away with the tide. One of them was my father, gone so long now he was only half a memory. The stranger didn't ask us any questions, just stared into the fire as if he was trying to see patterns in the flames.

He had been with us a week when Grandma started again with her first question – *Are ye a selkie? Where's yer seal skin? Hae ye come to tak Kirstie to yer summer hame?* I stared at her in disbelief as she finished and rested her hands in her lap. Sighing, I turned to the stranger and spoke aloud for her, repeating each of her questions and hiding none of my irritation.

He waited a full minute. Then he answered me.

'I hae no seal skin. But my hame is in the sea and I'll tak ye there if ye'll come.'

'In the sea? What do ye mean?' I said.

'Under the waves. An underwater palace, filled wi the treasure o' lost ships. Diamonds and rubies, gold coins and silver platters, fine glassware everywhere ye can see. All lit by curtains o' light.'

I stared at him. Eventually Grandma tapped me on the arm and gestured impatiently, demanding her answers.

'He said he's just a lost sailor and he'll be on his way soon enough,' I signed to her and she sat back with a look of disappointment.

'What happens if I go there?' I asked. 'Can I come back?'

'No,' he said. 'Ye can ne'er come back.'

*

Every time the stranger came into the room, I left. I didn't want his eyes on me, or his ramblings about underwater palaces to disconcert me. I sat with the hens, letting their soft clucking soothe me, and I walked on the beach, listening to the swash of the sea and the clack of the pebbles under my feet. But one day I turned away from the slate-grey waves to find him standing behind me.

'Kirstie,' he said, 'I'll be leaving soon. Will ye come wi me?'

I shook my head at him, folding my arms across my chest.

'Yer grandmother is an old woman. Soon ye'll be alone here,' he said, fixing me with his dark eyes and making my skin prickle.

'I'll no leave her,' I said. 'I'm all she has.'

He nodded. He let his eyes move past me and rest on a spot out on the waves. I scurried away from him and climbed the path to the cottage. Half way up I turned and look back. He was staring at the sea and in front of him the waves were dancing in a whirlwind, rising up as if a ferocious wind was whipping them into a frenzy.

*

That night I sat with Grandma and asked her to tell me the old tales. She started with the selkies, because she loved them, or the romantic idea of them. They would come to charm the land-women because they had cried into the sea, mourning a lost love.

But I wanted to know what else was out there. Who could stir up the waves with their mind?

Grandma's face grew clouded, her eyebrows knitted closer together, her hands signing the answers. The Finfolk were terrible sorcerers of the sea. They could control the sea and power a boat with their mind. And they wanted to steal people to take to Finfolkaheem, their home under the sea.

Perhaps she saw a flicker on my face, perhaps not. But next she told me that they loved silver; it was their obsession. Then she signed to me, *your grandfather's watch is in the dresser.* The stranger sat in the corner of the room silently watching our hands casting long dancing shadows on the walls.

The morning came with an unnatural quietness. I found Grandma in her bed, cold and skin waxy. My tears fell as I clasped her hands together. I stumbled out to the kitchen where the stranger was waiting for me.

'Will ye come wi me now, Kirstie?' he said.

I stared at him. His words – *'Soon ye'll be alone here'* – came back to me.

'Aye,' I told him. 'But we must dig a grave and bury her first.'

He turned and went outside. Within a few minutes I saw him walking up the grassy slope behind the cottage with a spade over his shoulder. I pulled my shawl around my shoulders and went to say my last farewell to my grandmother.

*

As I ran my lungs began to burn. Every muscle in my legs told me to stop but every emotion told me to run until I reached our rowing boat. My breathing was ragged by the time I was knee-deep and pushing the boat into the foamy water. My skirts were soaked and weighing me down as I hauled myself into the boat, my hands shaking as I found the oars and felt the rough wood under my palms. I dared not look at the beach until I was safely out on the water, rowing far out to sea.

Then, a shout.

'Kirstie, ye cannae get away!' The stranger was standing in a boat; a boat that moved by itself, by an unknown power. His tone was mocking me.

I pulled on the oars, feeling splinters torment me. The sound of blood rushing in my ears filled my head.

The distance between us shortened. He stood on his boat, gliding towards me while I rowed, trying to tell myself I was born of sea-farers, I could row hard enough. But with every stroke I completed he grew closer. Waves started to grow like walls around us, trapping me. A dreadful wind howled and my boat rocked like a fragile eggshell against the swell, water lapping over the sides.

His face broke into a sickening smile as he reached out to touch my boat. There was no time left. I reached into my pockets and felt for the cold heavy disc hidden there. I flung my grandfather's silver watch into the waves and watched the stranger's face transform. Stricken, he let out a cry and leapt under the water, leaving his boat spiralling.

Within moments the sea calmed and flattened, the wind dwindling to a breeze. I sat, dazed and exhausted. I watched his discarded boat drift away until it was a speck among the moving ridges of water. Then I picked up the oars, turned the boat around and rowed home.

Heather Parry

WET LIKE JELLY

It's strange looking into your son's eyes when they're staring back at you from inside some other kid's face. Uncanny. A bit odd. I could feel the cold sting of regret nip at my Achilles, truth be told, but there was no going back now. I had him. I'd taken him. He was my responsibility.

'D'ya want a biscuit?' I asked the lad.

'No,' he said, pointing Dylan's pupils at the floor. I got the Rich Tea out of the cupboard anyway and put them next to his cup. Dylan would probably have wanted a biscuit. His mam always had a sweet tooth.

'No!' he yelled, sending a cloud of crumbs flying into my face. I counted three and breathed out through my mouth slowly, wiping the mess from my lips. Weekends away, they were never easy. Once we got some food in us, we'd be more settled. Hunger does no one any favours.

I opened the fridge but there wasn't anything edible in there, only a pint of semi skimmed that might have been there since the millennium, going by the smell. My fault, really. I should have stopped on the drive up and got some basics. The place was hardly kid-friendly either. Not really a great start to this whole father–son thing. Still, we'd make it work. We'd have to. I said as much to the lad and he looked up at me with tears in Dylan's eyes and I damn near started crying right there and then.

*

They said it was a miracle of medical science that we could take our son's eyes out of his body and put them straight into another little baby. I asked why such a miracle couldn't have brought our kid back to life when he died for no reason inside my wife's belly at forty weeks, but the doctor just looked at his feet and my wife turned away and said 'Alan, don't,' as if it wasn't a bit hypocritical to be talking about miracles at a time like that. Three days later she was still in that ward, getting prodded and poked and smeared and whatnot, and the doctor thought it was a good idea to bring me the kid's fucking eyes, in some sort of medical container all covered in tubes and mechanics, as if to prove what a fucking miracle worker he was. They were blue, so light they were almost grey, just like my dad's, and they were so wet and like jelly that I wouldn't have been surprised if they'd looked right up at me. He held them out to me but I couldn't take the box.

'Alan, don't,' she said again when I started to tell that doctor that he'd ruined my little lad and he'd never be right again, and I'll be damned if a minute later she didn't have hold of that box like it was the boy himself. She'd have put it right to her breast if it had had a mouth. Sick started coming up in me and when I got outside I couldn't even light a fag, my hands were shaking so much. The box was gone when I got back upstairs.

*

'D'ya need a piss?' I asked the lad, wary that we'd come a long way and he might go down his legs and onto the kitchen chair. He said no and I asked him again, because sometimes they need prodding a bit, these kiddies; that's what my sister says at least and she's got five of the things. He still said no, and looked a bit bored, and I was trying to keep him on good terms so I let it go. He kicked his feet against the table, spilling my drink and his, creating a lake of watery tea beneath the mugs. He was definitely bored.

'So, what do you – you know . . . do? Usually?'

'What?'

'What do you do? When you're at home?'

'I don't know.'

'Well come on lad, you must have some idea.'

'I do Lego. Read books. Help Mum with the baby. I don't know.'

I looked at the musty rooms around us, the empty living room open to the kitchen. Nothing in here, nothing in there. The rest, a bust.

'So . . . telly?'

He sat himself on the sofa, releasing a breath of old decades from the material, and after a bit of tinkering I managed to get the Sky box on, flicked to some animated rubbish, feeling some sense of achievement. Then someone said fuck and I realised it was too late in the day for *Scooby-Doo*.

'Wait. Are you allowed to watch these?'

He ignored me, engrossed in the too-adult figures in front of him. I tried to sift through my head for rules and guidelines. Nothing.

'Are you sure you don't need a piss?'

He screamed in the negative, turning up the volume on his cartoons, so I found a can of warm lager from the cupboard and had myself a bit of a think.

Next time I looked over, there was a growing patch of piss on the crotch of his shorts. I grabbed him under the arms and ran him upstairs, kicked open the bathroom door and plonked him in front of the loo. He didn't move, and the darkness grew bigger.

'Can't you pull your pants down?' I ran through vague memories of dads in petrol station toilets, trying to remember whether they went in with their kids, and whether it was just the little ones that needed a hand, but – how little? How can you tell their age?

'It's not that!' The sob in it cut through me.

'Haven't you been . . . trained?'

'Shut the door, shut the door!'

He clutched his wet crotch and screamed the words, and when I slammed the bathroom door from the inside he only screeched louder. Outside, I listened for the trickle. Caught nothing. With five minutes gone I started to panic, thinking of heads down toilets and drownings in an inch of bath water and I kicked the locked door in, thinking him dead, but instead found him desperately weeping, wet clothes on the floor, him trying to wrap a dusty beige towel around his privates as if it was a nappy.

We had no spares, of course. Nothing in any of the wardrobes neither. Eventually I let him dry off his bits, put his pants and shorts on the back of a radiator and got him leg by leg into a used but dry pair of my old boxers that I found in my football bag in the back of

the car. I looked the place over for a safety pin to no avail, so he had
to make do with a clothes peg to keep them up. If he hadn't been
shaking quite so much, I might just have laughed.

I could prove myself a bit with dinner, I thought, but accidentally
chucked the jar of sauce on the floor, spilling most of it, sending
shards of glass scuttling everywhere under his tender little feet. He
cried a bit while I was cooking the pasta, proper crying too, biting
his bottom lip and wailing with his mouth shut, and it made my
hands shake because I'd never seen any of my kids crying. I thought
I might faint and that he'd get away, but he stopped after a while
and came and sat at the table to eat, yawning like it was well past
his bedtime. I offered him a bit of lager but he said no, so he had
weak tea with no milk and for afters we had a tin of peaches with
some squirty cream that had gone out of date. By turns he looked
dead scared and dead tired, and I realised I hadn't had cause to make
conversation with a six-year-old since I was a lad myself.

'What time's your bedtime?'

'Half seven. I mean – nine,' he said, eyes widening. Let him have
it, I thought. It's half eleven anyway. Cheeky little sod.

I looked all over for entertainment and found a pack of cards, just
forty-nine as it turns out, but I figured it didn't really matter, not for
a little one. We tried poker with pennies for chips, then gin rummy,
then twist, but it was all beyond him bar Snap, that tedium, and after
a couple of games he started kicking my shins and saying he was
bored. So telly it was, again, an action film with guns and titties;
damaging, no doubt, but at least it filled the long hour till he looked
tired enough to sleep.

'Do you need a story?'

'I'm not a baby you know. I'm in the Cubs. I've been camping in
the woods and everything.'

'It's not only babies need stories, my lad.'

'I haven't got my toothbrush. My mouth's dirty. You're bad at this.'

'Ni' mind son, them's only your baby ones,' I spat, blindsided by
the rage, the white burn, the horrible truth from this unexpected
carrier, the spite in my voice catching us both off guard, a slap without
physicality. 'They'll all fall out regardless, brush or no brush.' He

looked on the verge of tears again, which I didn't get, really, as it wasn't exactly a cruel thing to say, but seeing as how I was a couple of cans in and the upset had already started to subside, I had the urge to comfort him a bit.

'Look, we won't be here long at all, all right kidda? There's some Polo mints in the car if your mouth tastes like shite and you'll likely be home in a couple of mornings anyway.'

He was quieter after. The wind out of him. Washed his face without prompting, because I'd no idea to tell him, then got himself a blanket out of the cupboard. I hadn't realised it was cold. He was out like a light and I had a bit of a moment then, not just the guilt, the regret, but realising how I'd never seen my lad's eyes flicker shut at night, never seen them trying to fight off tiredness. When my lad came out his eyes were fused shut, just like all the ones before him. With normal dead babies you've to pry their eyelids open with a wet cotton bud so you can pretend that your baby's blinking and that they can have a nice look at their dadda. I didn't have any time to work on them eyes, though, not Dylan's. The next time I saw them they were in a fucking box in some doctor's hands, without any lids or lashes or sockets around them.

*

They asked us about the eyes just after they'd said he was dead. We'd said no on all the donor forms like usual and I thought it was a bit of a shit move, really, to ask that of a woman who'd just been told that another little 'un was going to come out of her dead and that she might as well stop trying. My wife leaned over her belly and signed the form before I'd even had a chance to say no. The doctor banged on about the transplant being a worldwide first as if that meant it wouldn't be so bad to drive home with an empty car seat again and have to tell all the neighbours that no, that massive bump stuck to the front of my wife for near on ten months hadn't ended up being anything good, and I couldn't even breathe for the thought that I wouldn't get that little body this time, I couldn't even protest, let alone rip up that form and tell that doctor to go fuck himself because we'd made them eyes. They were ours. I was paralysed with the thought of his little head with nothing in it.

She seemed all right, that was the worst of it. Once her insides were gone it was like she'd got a second wind, telling everybody that her baby was the baby whose eyes they'd taken out whole, first proper eye transplant an' all that, as if it was an achievement to have had one die. She kept all the paper cuttings in a little album and I had to say *love, this is getting a bit much, don't you think*, and she said *you better fuck off Alan because this is all I've got now, this is all people will remember of any of those kids. Because of this, my lad's life had a purpose. You've got your horrible little sideshow in the cellar and I've got this so you keep your mouth shut and I won't tell anyone about your project downstairs.* And I thought you wouldn't dare, you stupid cow, but I didn't say it, and it's when you don't say it that things start to go bad, isn't it? So a year later she'd moved back in with her mam and a year after that we were signing divorce papers and a year after that I'd lost my job, and they said it was just layoffs, more cuts, Alan, though we all knew it was because I came to work with fag-ends in my hair and breath that was forty per cent proof.

*

I watched some more telly with another couple of cans. All gambling phone-in shows and reruns of programmes that were shit twenty years ago, but it was a good bit of noise to drown out the crying. A constant wail, I couldn't stop it, the sound only cutting out when I took another sip of beer. *Bad at this*, I thought, and it was right, and I begged then, in my head at least, for them to hurry up and get here. I wanted done with it. I wanted it over, couldn't do it. Failure. I wanted rescue.

The only thing that calmed me was the realisation that they must already be halfway here.

The woman at the transplant centre had probably let the police know that I'd been there asking questions, as I'd had a bit of a breakdown in the foyer and she had to have security put me back in my car. A green Nissan Micra with a busted rear window wouldn't be that hard to find, and we'd had to stop for a piss and a packet of crisps more than once on the way up so we must have been seen. If they'd got into my flat and found Isaac and Emma and Tess and all the other kids in the airing cupboard then they'd be after me like a mad dog after a rabbit anyway, given that all them little floating bodies had eyes and our Dylan's didn't. Seven little kids all perfectly formed and only our Dylan without his fucking eyes. There was no cellar for them at my new flat but I thought they'd likely be warmer near the boiler anyway. I'd stopped looking at them so much in the last few weeks. It was too hard to see Dylan standing out from all his brothers and sisters. I hadn't even been able to get the right type of jar for him, as they'd stopped selling that kind just before we got pregnant that last time. The others had clear glass and his was green, so he looked like the little freak of the family, with his green glass jar and his empty head. If police had got into the flat they'd take one look at them empty sockets and think about our Dylan's eyes in this little lad's head and be after me like I was the bloody Moors murderer. Just a few more hours, then, fingers crossed.

I wondered if the kid might have to get up in the night to have a cry or a piss or whatever but when I looked in it was near on three and he was still dead to the world. Mouthy little shite, really. I touched his blond hair and watched his shoulders go up and down every time he took in a breath. Dylan wouldn't have been mouthy. Dylan wouldn't have been blond. His mam's grandma was from Trinidad and our family's all mousey brown, so Dylan would have had thick dark hair that would have been a bugger to comb. You could see a bit of it when he came out, though it was all stuck to his skull and there wasn't much of it anyway, and these days he was bald as a cue ball. When they've been in formaldehyde for a while all their fuzz falls off, all their eyelashes and that fur they get inside their mam's belly. Black hair and blue eyes: he would have been a killer, our Dylan. A mild-mannered lady killer, never talking back to his dad or pissing in his pants or making it hard to raise him.

I'd had it in my head that this lad would have had thick black hair too, so when I got a look at him in the playground with all that yellow hair I thought I'd got the wrong kid. It was all right once I finally got hold of him and put him in the car. He was just quiet really, and so was I, but when we got on the M1 I started to think about what I'd done and I went a bit loopy if I'm honest, talking to the lad and saying it's all right Dylan we're not going far Dylan we're just going to have a little holiday Dylan. The lad started weeping and I had to lock him in the car for a bit and leave it on the hard shoulder and have a wander until I gathered myself back up again.

*

I found some grey gin at the back of the pantry as it was getting light and poured it all into a pint glass. I'd decided by then; if there was no sign of them by noon, I'd drive us both in. Put this whole thing to bed. Get the fucking thing over with. I couldn't imagine what I'd been thinking in the first place, couldn't remember the thought process that had led me to that spot, with some kid that I had never known, playing a role I didn't know how to play.

The lad came down about half six, wiping sleep out of Dylan's eyes and asking if he could have a glass of water, so I got him one and put some of last night's pasta in a bowl. He sat across from me, spilling sauce onto the table, knocking water on the floor, and I thought he's a stranger, this lad. Someone else's little boy. A little troublemaker, really. Dylan would have been a good 'un, although me and his mam wouldn't have been all that good at bringing him up. We'd never had the practice. Never had the patience. Not even with each other, really. Too much anger and not even love. Probably for the best, really. I probably would have had to bury all them other bodies if he'd lived. It's a bit maudlin and all that, having dead kids near where your live kid sleeps, and I wasn't really ready to bury all them kids yet. My real kids. Polished glass, clear liquid, no bother at all.

I drained the gin. Watched the kid finish his pasta. Then, as it was all getting fuzzy and I could hear all the sirens coming through the woods, I grabbed the lad and kissed his eyes and held him and let my tears fall onto his blond hair.

Rachel Plummer

THE WOMAN WHO MARRIED HADRIAN'S WALL

I adored from the start
the way his stones drew heat
from my hands to the earth. The way
they split like baleen in the land's jaw.

There was something in the way he held himself –
as if it was only stubbornness that kept him
from giving in to the wind.

It was the strength in his broad back.
The taste of lichens.

It was sturdy Scottish legs, bare,
straddling the border below
that classic Roman profile.

It was something barbarian
in him, something held back. As if
he might burst like a dam and all Scotland
would come flooding out.

At first I touched him
reverently, each crevice
or crack, moss patch or spider's egg sack,
each woodlouse.
I felt him sigh, settle
deeper into the ground.

We eloped to Gretna.
After almost two thousand years
I felt he'd waited long enough.

That night I dreamt of sinking
into the vallum, eroding
like a boundary – all softness slowly
weathered from my bones.

Sharon Gunason Pottinger

ON A CAROLINA BREEZE

for C.B.

Here on the ragged grey coast
on a day between weathers
the air so still the wingbeat of a passing bird
becomes loud as a thunderclap,
I climb Dunnet Head and watch the sea birds
beneath me dive and squabble and soar
for the joy of flying the hot air currents.
I can see the Merry Men of Mey
dancing in the rip tide and Stroma in profile
golden pink and grey in the bright light.
I cannot see all the way across the broad
blue sea back home, but I look anyway.

The wind blows in from the west
warm and soft as magnolia petals
in a Carolina springtime and I remember
a barefoot girl pushing so hard on an old
porch swing that the chains clanked
and her grandmother fretted,
but she pushed til her toes no longer
touched the ground for the love of flying
in the cool morning air before the heat
rose to fill everything overfull and
ice melted in the sun tea and pink lemonade
leaving long trails of cool water
like waterfalls down the edge of the glass
then waiting for the darkness to see
lightning bugs rise from the dew
on the twilight grass to flash their love songs
and hear crickets sing to the moon.

When the fickle wind shifts, I'll pluck a clip of wool
from a lonely fence left by a passing ewe
and send it back to you, full of peat smoke
and heather scent, a breath of cool sea air
in the heat shimmer of a sultry day.
You'll feel the pull of the tides of a distant sea
and remember the days between weathers
of rare light and stillness
where drivers smile and wave in a do si do
on narrow roads like bare strings
through a tapestry of greens and greys
and nights are quiet beneath a broad black sky
awash with ice white stars.

Julie Robertson

A NOTE OF INTEREST

Over the years I had driven past the house, telling myself the road was a shortcut. As soon as I saw the For Sale sign I had pulled in and called the estate agent. Now, I was standing in front of the door, my heart racing under my silk blouse and cashmere coat. Harry, my husband, would be on the golf course, oblivious to the fact that I had never felt so alive in years.

The door opened. Yes, it was the poet. A bit raddled, still wearing black eyeliner, lipstick bleeding into tiny tributaries around her mouth.

'Mrs Marshall?'

I started at my married name. I only kept it for off-colour legal transactions when my clients were dodgier than usual. Today it would come in handy.

'Yes, that's me. Sorry I'm a bit late.'

There had only been one girl at the checkout of the supermarket that I had gone into en route. No one in the long queue had volunteered to let me go ahead with the single item that I had wanted to purchase. They all stood, eyeing up my expensive clothes.

I patted the side of my handbag and felt the shape of the tub inside.

'You're the first,' she said.

Dark William Morris wallpaper, peacock feathers in a lustre vase. Still such a hippy. She led me about the house from room to room. Inherited wealth must be dwindling now – poetry prize money and literature grants don't pay for maintenance work. No cleaner, either – I noticed dust on the antiques and stoor under the furniture. The heavy dark furniture would have belonged to the Austrian Jewish grandparents, the ones who suffered from survivor guilt. I had read all about them in interviews that she had given and, of course, in the poems.

The poems – the ones that I had enjoyed most were the poems about Alex, the love of her youth, her male muse – dark and delicious, lean and mean, Alex whose tender love-making and cruel infidelities cropped up – disguised, veiled but always there like a breathing body.

*

Alex, my first husband. He was the reason I was here, wearing a wig that I had spent most of the previous week searching for – a natural-looking one – I had to get the parting right.

I caught sight of myself in a foxed mirror. Newly purchased eyeshadow and foundation complemented the caramel-coloured streaked hair. I kept waiting to see if there was a hint of recognition in her eyes. None. Had I aged so much? Then I reminded myself that, if she had ever seen me, it would have been from a distance – the young wife with the baby in the pushchair, waiting in a Byres Road café for her Ulysses to return from his literary adventures. And his sexual ones. It took me a while to realise what he was up to. A note folded neatly in the doorjamb of his office had finally, irrevocably confirmed it.

'You left your copy of *The Wasteland* under the bed. Was hoping to give it back to you in person. Glad you enjoyed our conference! Love Amy.'

And now, thirty years later, the author of the note stood in front of me, waffling on about the view of the river from the dining room window. There was no mention of the work needing done: the stains on the wallpaper, the bulge in the ceiling above the bay window, the gaps in the skirting boards. I smiled at her as I looked at the cornices.

It did not take long to find out why she was leaving the beautiful rotting house.

'I am reconnecting with my past,' she said, 'I suppose I really owe it all to Facebook.'

'Really,' I said. 'Old friends?'

'The love of my life, really.' She giggled, twisting a long strand of greying hair around her finger.

My suspicions were right. Over the last ten years, Alex had kept up a perfunctory long-distance relationship with our daughter.

Occasionally she would allow me to scan over his posts and photographs of him – once a dark-haired Adonis, now bald but bearded.

He looked avuncular and erudite – just the way a professor in a North American university should look. He would be as happy as Larry – surrounded by coteries of adoring students within easy access of mountains. He loved to hike and posted up photographs of himself and women with expensive smiles standing on mountain summits. Recently the posts had thinned out.

Amy was in full flow. '—I was asked to read at Poetry Festival at Ashland and this man, an old flame, was on the bill, too. I could not believe it. We had such a great time. And now – well – I am throwing my lot in with him.'

'Could I possibly have another look around?' I said.

'Of course,' she said trying to sound businesslike. 'I will be in the kitchen.'

I wandered back into the sitting room where the shelves heaved under the weight of the books. Scanning along the shelves, I found it – *The Wasteland*, nestled between the anthologies. I pulled out the book by its spine and opened it. Inside, I saw my handwriting: 'To Alex, love from Gerda.'

She never could have given it back to him in person. I had torn up the incriminating note that I had found in the door. She must have felt rejected, ignored, demeaned. But nowhere near as bad as I did, that day as I sat alone in Kelvingrove Park with a bottle of cheap champagne. It would have been our first anniversary. It was our last.

For a moment, I thought about leaving out the book on top of a brass Indian table in the centre of the room but I pushed it back flush against the others.

Then, I set to work, fishing out plastic gloves from my bag. I snapped them on, took the top off a tub of tiny grey pink prawns and jammed them into the nooks and crannies of the woodwork around the windows, down the sides of the skirting boards, under the heavy furniture, between the floorboards. Patricia Cornwell would have been impressed. When I had finished, I slipped off the gloves and put them in a plastic bag along with the empty tub inside my handbag. I tiptoed into the loo to wash off any trace of the smell of prawns from my fingers. I could not resist looking into the bathroom cabinets – they were all clear – she must have moved the antidepressants and the herbal remedies.

When I returned to the kitchen, Amy was sitting with a cup of coffee, flicking through a magazine.

'Beautiful house,' I said.

'Yes, there should be a lot of interest. It should sell quickly. Do you want to see the garden?'

She unlocked the door and I wandered around the paths bordered by overgrown plants. A fence bounded the garden before the ground sloped down to the river. That narrowed the market down a bit – no parents in their right minds would be bidding for this house.

I walked back into the kitchen.

'Any problems with damp?' I asked.

'No,' she frowned.

She was not good at lying. Damp-coursing would be a definite. I knew from surveyors' reports for the flats along the street that I had bought for landlord clients and money launderers.

'Vermin?'

She looked alarmed. 'No.'

'Well,' she said, 'there is another viewing in five minutes. Is that you, then?'

I was irritating her, angering her now.

'Yes, thank you,' I said, walking towards the front door. I turned around as I left.

'I'll put in a note of interest.'

'Oh, that is good,' she said, warming a little.

'I will want a second viewing.'

'Great,' she smiled.

Yes, I thought, I would need a second viewing to plank some bags of heroin next time. I sat in my car outside and scrolled down my list of contacts – Mad Frank from Possil would do nicely.

Cynthia Rogerson

SHE WASN'T PRETTY

They married and built their own house on a plot surrounded by fields and woods, with the closest house about half a mile away, just visible. The process, from breaking ground to moving in, took just over a year. They spent weekends sanding, painting, varnishing, digging, choosing kitchen units, wall colours, floorings, and here they were at last. About to go to bed for the first night in their new house.

Some of the rooms were empty still, and the living room was full of boxes and bags. But their bedroom was already a nest. Candles burned on the window sill – curtain-less because who needs curtains when there are no neighbours? The bed was new, but the patchwork quilt was old. Her grandmother had sewed the patches from Edwina's childhood dresses, and each had a memory. The house smelled new – of paint, and fresh timber and varnish. But this room smelled most strongly of lavender because, like her name, Edwina was old-fashioned. All her body products had this scent, and so, of course, did the candles. Jeb was a Johnson's Baby Powder and tea-tree man, and those were the undernotes to the lavender.

They bathed this first night – first her, then him in the same water. They washed each other's back and neck, and hummed and sometimes sang snippets of songs. She favoured old musicals, while he preferred modern singer-songwriters. Like the lavender, tea-tree and Johnson's, the combination worked somehow. Then they got into bed. Because they were used to each other now, no longer insatiable, they lay not touching at first. Just resting side by side, head on pillows. Jeb picked up his Kindle.

'Just think,' she whispered, looking at the candle flame reflected in the dark window.

'What.' Not whispering, still reading.

'No one else in the history of mankind has slept in exactly this space. I am certain I have never in my entire life slept in a place that had not already been slept in.'

'Huh.'

'Jeb. It's as if this is the house's wedding night. Tonight it'll lose its virginity.' She giggled. So risqué of her!

'I guess you could be right. Maybe this will be the first time anyone's slept here. Though there's no way to know for certain. Human beings have been around a long time.'

'Well, maybe so. But not exactly here.'

'Why? How do you know?'

'Because we are upstairs. In the distant olden days, which are the only days in which people might have lived here, everyone slept on the ground.' Not whispering now either. A little annoyed because he always took things so literally, and he hadn't laughed at her joke. He needed everything to be accurate. It was irritating, suddenly.

A pause. She turned on her side, away from him. He closed his Kindle and sighed.

'What about those ten-storey buildings in Edinburgh? Those are from medieval times. Or older.'

Another pause. She turned on her back and he picked up his Kindle again.

'Well, okay,' she said. 'But that was the city. Edinburgh had already existed by then. This is a hillside in the middle of nowhere. The soil's not even good enough for crops.'

'Your point?'

'It is highly unlikely, in fact impossible, that people built tall houses here, which have left no trace.' Using her teacher voice now. Prim and instructive. He shuffled himself further up the bed, till he was sitting straight up. Had she ever spoken to him like this before?

Pause. She noted, but did not remark on, the creaking of their new house. As if it was still getting used to its own existence, and did not yet understand its own limitations or size. As if it was breathing. This made her shiver deliciously.

'Crap, Edwina. Seems a bit . . . arrogant. To claim you know that.'

She pressed her lips together. He'd never used this tone before. Almost aggressive. And there was no need to swear. Or to use her full name. For heaven's sake! She tisked loudly, and groaned a little.

'Everyone knows it, Jeb.'

'Everyone?'

'Yes, ask anyone. Phone someone right now. Your mother.'

'My mother?'

'Yes. Your mother. She knows everything.'

'Says who?'

'Says you. You think she knows everything.'

'Is this about your wedding flowers again?'

This felt like a hard slap, and her love for him shrivelled up inside her chest. Sizzled like a drop of water thrown on a hot frying pan.

'I never complained about the flowers.'

'No, but you wanted to.'

'You couldn't know that. I smiled. I said thank you.'

'Yeah, but you did that thing you do. With your mouth.'

'What thing?'

'You really don't know?'

'Why would I ask if I knew?'

'I don't know. You have your little tactics to avoid friction. To avoid confrontation, but still make your views known.'

Silence. Her heart pounded. These accusations hit at her very nature, and were not answerable. If he'd said she never put the rubbish out, or she could wear a bit more lipstick – those were the kind of things that could be fixed, but not this. This was the end of their marriage, this had to mean the end. She could feel her face flushing. How would she explain this to her parents? Her colleagues? The postman? She was momentarily glad she hadn't yet changed her passport.

Three minutes passed, while their new house yawned and sunk minutely into the foundations. They faced away from each other, and wiggled their bottoms so not even a buttock was touching.

Tragic, of course, but so inevitable she had to admit to a small measure of relief in her pain. No more waiting and wondering how it would end. It was over right now, and she could take back her rightful role of spinster. She was not pretty; no man had ever flirted with her before Jeb. She scanned the bedroom, pictured packing all the things she considered hers. Bickering over the wedding presents, like the towels and the china and that wonderful little landscape by a local artist. Lochardil Beach.

'Are you crying, Edie?'

'No.'

'Jesus, you are so. Why are you crying?'

Pause. She blew her nose and didn't know whether to be angry or philosophical with him. Did it matter any more? Something so liberating about being at the end of things. She could just be herself now, right? Nothing to lose any more.

'Because it's not fair.' Indignantly, having chosen anger. 'It's not!' she spat at him.

'You're not making sense. What's not fair?'

'Don't act innocent now. Why should you get to keep Lochardil Beach, when it's only me who loves it? You just think it's an investment. You don't, you don't . . .' pause while she hiccupped. 'Love it! You don't love it. You don't . . .'

'Are you talking about that painting we got when we got married? From my cousin?'

She nodded, too overcome now to trust speaking. Her face streaked with tears and snot. He moved towards her. Pulled her in to him, but she would not look at him.

'Ah, Edie, you are silly. That painting belongs to both of us, and neither of us is going anywhere. I hope. Is this because I mentioned the wedding flowers?'

She nodded. Sniffing. Silence for a full minute. He stroked her hair, and she couldn't help but enjoy this. The fact it might be the last time he touched her hair gave it poignancy.

'Why do you hate me?' She had to ask. It had to be asked.

'I do not hate you. Edwina. Oh Edie. I love you, twit face. But you get so intense and you always exaggerate. It can get a little annoying.'

She turned away, and her shoulders heaved with silent sobs again.

'Jesus, I hope you're not going to still be like this when we have children.'

'How are we going to have children, if we're divorced?' she managed to croak.

'Stop it, Edie. You are . . . exhausting. And I am . . .'

'Shush!' She sat up and touched his mouth. 'Listen, what was that?'

Pause. Then a sudden guttural noise outside.

'A dog barking?'

'Except there are no dogs here.'

It came again. If a cow and lion could produce a hybrid, this was the sound it would make. A low roar, but no aggression – ending in a sad, drawn-out bovine lowing. They crept out of bed and peeked out of the window. Once they blew out the candle, the night did not seem dark at all. In fact, it was a bright night, with a three-quarter moon hanging yellow and lumpish.

'I don't see any dogs.'

The sound came again, closer and from more than one source. It seemed to be right outside their house. Jeb slowly opened the window, and suddenly the shadows in their field resolved themselves into deer. Red deer, tall and rangy. Half a dozen hinds, in the patch of field about to become their garden. They were not close to each other, but now they all froze in the same direction, their white bottoms pointed to the house.

'I can smell them. Can you smell them?' Edwina whispered.

'Yeah. They stink.'

After a minute, the deer began feeding again. She could hear them breathing and tugging grass and chewing. The strange low roaring came again, but not from the hinds, who ignored it and carried on eating. It came from three stags, loitering on the hill just above the house. Then came the sound of hooves pounding turf, briefly, and a sudden clattering as antlers crashed into each other.

'Are they killing each other?' she asked, thrilled.

'No. Just figuring out who gets to be the boss. The daddy.'

The hinds still did not pause in their grazing. Jeb and Edwina stood there, close enough to touch shoulders, and after a while he closed the window and they went back to bed. They cuddled for warmth. She had lost her angry and frightened feeling, but nothing rushed in to replace it. This is where the deer probably always came this time of year, she thought, and maybe our house being here now made no difference to them. She imagined how this place had been, for years. For centuries. Thousands of centuries. Forested, wild, cold.

Wild animals, now long extinct, had grazed right here. Maybe it was true and there had, after all, been another dwelling here before. Maybe an entire village, full of noisy children and yipping dogs and brawling red-faced men. Maybe their own house too would vanish. First it would become unoccupied, then it would decay, crumble, and eventually the earth would reclaim it. She saw their two pale bodies, suspended horizontally in air, where their bedroom used to be a million years ago. Maybe this moment of feeling nothing but the new coldness between them, would last a long, long time. No one knew these things.

They'd not been pretty, the hinds. Not like Bambi. Their faces were long and moose-like. Their fur was mangy. Somehow she'd never thought of deer as wild animals – rough, smelly and slightly unnerving. Not at all how they looked from a distance. Maybe it was the same with love. Prettier from a distance.

Jeb closed his Kindle, gathered her into his arms and yawned deeply as if none of their conversation had taken place. Was he really so shallow? Or worse, was he a simpleton? Nevertheless, she noted his warmth, his naturalness. His hand strayed to her thigh and stroked it lazily. This was his way of asking. She felt acutely aware of him, but not aroused yet. If her marriage had not ended, it had at least profoundly altered course and she would need to pay closer attention now. She could feel her heart reconfigure itself around this new knowledge, as if molecules of love had been added or taken away. She wasn't sure which. She'd wanted a man to love and here he was.

Helen Sedgwick

THE ARCHAEOLOGIST OF AKROTIRI

It was the last of our family holidays. That I remember. Different from the rest because there was no caravan in Northumberland, no shared bunk-beds or suitcase of damp clothes, no windswept days marching Hadrian's Wall or struggling to pin down a picnic blanket on a rocky beach that was hairy with seaweed. It was the last of our family holidays and so in a final and, I see now, hopeful attempt to appease my sisters and me, my parents booked a small villa for a week on Santorini.

From the boat the island was a cliché – blue and more blue everywhere, the sky and sea perfectly still in their expanse, every precariously balanced house painted in spotless postcard white to stand out against the volcanic rock. Our villa was half way up, looking out towards the peaks and troughs of Crete. We had a small pool in the front garden from which, when I chose to ignore the insects floating on its surface, I could imagine there was nothing below me or behind me and look out to the Mediterranean as if I was alone in my bird's-eye view.

The first few days are now a blur. I think I spent most of the time floating in the pool, being aloof with my parents and ignoring my sisters. I was the one, as the eldest and the only boy, who had threatened to skip the holiday, persuaded to join them only by the sunshine and promise of my own room at long last. I had memorised a few words of Greek and thought that made me entirely independent, overlooking the fact that I had no money whatsoever. But after a few days my parents, determined for us to spend time together as a family, booked us on a tour of the island by minibus.

I remember a gold-dripped Orthodox church for which my Real Madrid shorts had to be corrected with a sarong, wrapped around my waist and tied in a knot at my side. There were photo stops, where the minibus pulled up into a space that looked like it would never fit us, and everyone but me piled out, took an identical photo of the view, then piled back in again. The minibus had a microphone that the tour guide used to tell us local history, but with my Walkman at full blast I couldn't tell you what information she conveyed. It was at around lunchtime, five hours after our eight a.m. start, that we were given our first, and only, choice.

Most of our group, my parents and sisters included, opted for a lazy lunch in a beachside café, to pass the hottest hours of the day under the shade of umbrellas with a cold drink and perhaps a salad of large ripe tomatoes and feta cheese. But I chose to accompany a different tour guide, a friend of our minibus driver, to the little-known archaeological site of Akrotiri.

*

We drove in a Land Rover along a single-track path, past half-built hotels that were nothing more than square shells of concrete, winding up the hill until we arrived at a dusty car park and left the four-by-four to continue on foot. A short walk led us to the edge of the cliffs, then in single file we made our way down the metallic temporary-looking steps that led to the site. From half way down, all that was visible were a number of trenches dug deep into the hillside, each one marked with red and white striped tape. The land was barren; the driest earth I had ever seen. As we turned and descended further I was able to make out fragments of stone walls jutting from the yellow soil on either side, but it wasn't until the final set of steps down that I realised what I was looking at. Below me were the remains, in brick and path and home, of an ancient ghost town.

The stones that jutted out from the earth started at foot level and continued far over my head, horizontal layers clearly marking different stories of the buildings. On the ground were the streets, indicated both by low-lying walls that seemed to be the original gutters and by modern wooden posts designating the different paths between the buildings. In places intact walls remained, the faded outlines and colours of frescoes still visible through the shadow – the only light came from the sun directly overhead. On one wall, a pair of blue monkeys were flying over a fiery sea. On another I could make out dozens of boats, each carrying dozens of people to a far-off destination.

I wandered the paths, stepping into one building after another, through internal halls and into courtyards, noticing small square rooms that could have been bedrooms, even finding a body-length stone slab that might once have been someone's bed. Occasionally a square hole in the wall let the light peer in, casting patterns on the dust floor or illuminating painted walls so faded I hadn't realised there was decoration on them at all: two painted men sat facing one another; a woman with papyrus; a banquet of fish. The longer I stared, the more colours I could see in the paintings of the lives of the inhabitants of Akrotiri. In the distance I could hear voices in Greek, one of which belonged to my tour guide, so I followed the sound along the street and past one of the bigger buildings that must have been owned by a local politician or rich businessman.

A larger trench to my left revealed the current site, and down in the ground a team of men and women, many of whom looked like students, were kneeling or squatting in the dust, painstakingly brushing away the earth to reveal another layer of walls and rooms beneath the ground I was standing on. In amongst them was my guide, talking quickly to one of the older men, who was holding a small trowel. He looked up towards me and made a gesture with his free hand that might have been beckoning me down to them or, more likely, telling me to go the other way. I continued along the path I had been on before, treading carefully over loose stones and debris, which I now suspect may well have been the kind of priceless artifacts that some of us spend our lives searching for. When I got to the end the path led abruptly into a bank of earth. I heard some footsteps behind me and turned, noticing as I did so the large area about six foot beneath me to my right.

The girl came to an abrupt stop beside me, tracking my gaze down to what appeared to be a pillared courtyard, presumably the town centre, paved with mosaics.

'That's the agora,' she said.

She was wearing trainers that could have once been white but were now the yellow-brown of the earth, a pair of dusty trousers and a coffee-coloured t-shirt that said something in Greek that I couldn't read.

'I speak the best English of everyone here,' she said. 'So I can tell you about things.'

'Are you learning English at school?' I asked her, conscious of the few years between us that made her still a child, while I had managed to convince myself that I was already an adult.

'Of course,' she said, talking a swig out of the dusty water bottle she was carrying with her. She looked at me as though waiting for me to come alive.

'What's behind there?' I gestured to the vertical bank of earth that prevented us from continuing down along the main street.

'The sea,' she said. 'We can't dig any more that way, or it will come down. Fall down.'

I didn't quite believe her. What could she know, after all? She was just a kid.

'Where's the rest of the town then?'

'In the sea.'

She took another swig of her water, and glanced over her shoulder to see that my tour guide was approaching us.

'What happened? I mean . . .?' I looked at the guide, over the girl's head.

'It is dated from 1600 BC.'

'Oh.'

'That is when the volcano erupted.'

'What volcano?'

'The island,' she said, gesturing around her. 'When the volcano erupted there was lava and pumice that buried the town, but also an earthquake. So half was buried, here, and half is under the sea, there.'

The girl was looking at me as if I was stupid.

'The Thera eruption,' she said.

'Was everyone killed?' I asked her, thinking that might bring her back on side.

She shrugged. 'There are no bodies. So we don't know. Yet.'

I looked back at the guide, who was looking down at the girl and smiling. 'She is right,' she said. 'The excavations haven't revealed a single body. They think that maybe they knew what was coming and escaped in boats. But it also might be that they were all in the other part of the town, or hiding somewhere they thought was safe that hasn't been excavated yet.'

'Like in Herculaneum?' I asked, pleased that at last I could offer something sensible.

'Exactly,' said the girl. 'Are you learning about the Romans in school?' Instead of waiting for a response she finished the last of her water and scrunched up the bottle.

'Phaedra is here every day over the summer,' the guide explained to me, looking from me to the girl and back again. 'Her father is the lead scientist on the team.'

'Yes,' Phaedra said. 'It is experience for when I grow up.'

'What do you want to be when you grow up?' I asked her

She didn't even hesitate; she just stared at me and said:

'I want to be the archaeologist of Akrotiri.'

The tour guide laughed then in a way that I will always remember as being incredibly unfair. I suppose to her Phaedra was just a precocious child who needed to be reminded that archaeologists work in teams, that there's never just one, that she couldn't be the only person in the centre of her future. It made me cross though, at the time, and it still does today. My tour guide had missed the point. Her laughter made Phaedra turn and walk away from us, but that was the moment I realised that she knew exactly what she wanted to be. And it involved a search for missing people who had died nearly four thousand years ago. To me, that seemed amazing.

On my way out I passed them again, the team working on the excavation, and Phaedra was down there with them. She was talking animatedly with the man who had waved at me earlier and I could see how alike they were in words and looks and posture. She didn't notice me go; why would she, when she had her father standing next to her?

After we got back to the café to meet up with all the other minibus tourists there were only ten minutes left for me to buy a can of Coke from a vending machine and a spinach pie from one of the self-service shops and then we had to continue on our tour. There was a monastery, I think, and a man who sold honey by the roadside, but I was still underground in the hidden streets and buried rooms of Akrotiri. For the rest of our holiday I like to think I was less sullen and withdrawn than I had been before, but that might be my age wanting to cast my younger self in a better light than I deserve. I looked for Phaedra around the island, on the beaches, in cafés and over-packed shops, but I never saw her again. We went home, I bickered with my sisters, my parents nagged me to do something useful for the rest of the summer and I resisted. But the next year I began my A-levels and I did well enough, as these things go, and gradually I did turn into the adult I had imagined I already was.

*

I remember being in a crowded tutorial a few years later, asking my lecturer about Akrotiri, and the slight scoff that accompanied his reply. No international teams were allowed to work on the site, he said with a shrug. Underpinning his nonchalance was frustration, I think, that one of the most important sites to have been discovered in recent history was forbidden to him and most other academics. The extent of the town itself, buildings of three and four stories, beautifully preserved frescos, a drainage system that almost outdid the modern equivalent, Linear A inscriptions, all predating Pompeii by sixteen hundred years at least, was locked away from him. It was no wonder the lack of a major international effort made him dismissive, but in a way I was glad. It kept it sacred. To me, Phaedra was still a disheveled twelve-year-old, scrambling around that ghost town looking for the lost inhabitants. I couldn't help pushing him a little further on the subject. 'Do you think it might be the lost city of Atlantis?' I asked him, wanting the possibility of a little magic to enter into our dry, practical lesson. I got only a sigh in return. We were scientists, and there was no place for ghosts and fairytales in our world.

In the years that followed I searched through journals regularly, looking for new discoveries, but there was barely a publication referring to Akrotiri. Colleagues I spoke to on digs around the world often looked at me blankly when I said the name. I focused on South American archaeology for my postgrad, and married a researcher from Cambridge whom I met on a dig in Ecuador. For our first anniversary she tracked down an out-of-print book written by a Greek archaeologist who had been researching the possible sites of Atlantis. It mentioned in passing the site at Akrotiri, saying simply that there was much still to be discovered.

In the end I stumbled across the news while researching holiday destinations for a much-needed break after our daughter was born. I thought perhaps I could go back to Santorini, see it with my own family as a grown man, but I was wrong. Akrotiri was closed. No further excavations would be done, no public visitors were allowed. A temporary roof over the site had collapsed, bringing down with it several of the ancient buildings and burying one of the archaeologists under the rubble. There was a link to a website that was no longer in use. No date to tell me when the accident had taken place.

I made phone calls and tried every contact I had who specialised in the Minoan era. I needed to know what had happened. Eventually I got through to an academic from Athens University, who confirmed what I had suspected.

'Balios Mikos was killed,' she said. 'He was the lead archaeologist on the site.'

'How awful.'

'Even worse, to not find the body.'

'What do you mean?'

'It seems he must have fallen into the sea, with several of the buildings.'

He was with the inhabitants, perhaps, under water along with the rest of the lost city of Akrotiri.

'It's all closed, then? There'll be no more excavation?'

'Oh no, it's starting again, with a new team. They're digging to the east of the town. They hope to find the boat houses.'

'Like in Herculaneum,' I said, with a smile that she couldn't see.

I could hear something happening on the end of the line, perhaps students arriving to see her or a colleague wanting to talk.

'Got to go,' she said. 'Hope I helped.'

'Wait, one second, please . . .'

'Yes?'

'Who is on the research team, do you know?'

'Not sure of the names, except the lead, Phaedra Mikos.'

'Phaedra?'

My query needed no more words than her name.

'Yes, that's right. You noticed the surname. She's his daughter.'

*

I see Akrotiri sometimes as it was before. I see buildings rising up from bustling streets, busy with the noise of vendors selling the fish they caught that morning, with poets and philosophers reciting their verse on street corners, local people gathered around to hear their words. I see richly decorated rooms full of people, tables of olives and wine, frescos of ships and heroes and saffron. And I see a volcano raining fire and ash through a blackened sky as people run through their homes, through the streets and to the sea where their ships wait to take them safely away from their devastated home. In my mind there is a place on board for every inhabitant, plus one more, who was to join them millennia later.

My daughter says sometimes that she wants to holiday in the sun. Her friends go to Spain, or Italy, or the south of France, but we prefer a caravan in Northumberland where we can face the wind and walk hand-in-hand along Hadrian's Wall. Sometimes we drive south, to camp in Cornwall or search for fossils on the beaches of Lyme Regis and Charmouth. This year we are planning a tour of Barra, Lewis and Skye, where the sea will be golden-grey and the landscape a wild canvas of purples and greens.

I'll never go back to the perfect white and blue of Santorini, on holiday or to work, and I hope that the rest of the world leaves it alone as well. It's not our site, and they are not our ghosts. They are hers. Sometimes, on a dig in Mexico or at the end of another term's teaching, someone will ask what drives me to do it, why I chose this career, why I spend my life searching for lost worlds. I say it is a fascination with history, the satisfaction that comes from solving a problem, or a search for cultures that have been forgotten. The last one is the closest to the truth, I suppose. But it took me a long time to realise that I'm doing all this because of the Archaeologist of Akrotiri.

Harry Smart

ANEMONE NEMOROSA

There are two greens of woodland that I love.
The first when the leaves of a beech wood break:
if you discount the pale grey-knuckled bole
and look into the middle levels

the branches shift and slant, all almost-horizontals.
On a bright day, when the leaves are barely out of bud,
the light goes through them sharp and green, as acid
as a half-ripe lime, and travels, glassy to the heart.

By early June, beneath the big loose canopy,
when wood anemones have flowered and set seed,
if you pick the tiny jesters' heads
they disintegrate and seeds the shape of apple pips

a quarter of the size of tears, soft creamy green,
slip between your fingers like ripe grain.

Graeme Stones

SPERM WHALE ASHORE

In its shade I shrank child-high,
Unsettled in a way
Not easy to account for.
It was not the teeth.
Those, in jaws squid-scarred,
Were curiously gentle.
Nor the elephantine smallness
Of its eye.
Nor just the bulk, the slabs
On which sea-grasses grew.
Nor yet what Ahab called
The unappeasable brow.

Someone, standing where I stood,
Had gashed that hide of supple slate.
I thought it simply spite
At first and then
Remembered Ahab once again
Astride the whale,
Blindly seeking
With a six-inch blade
The six-foot deep
Unfathomable heart.

Judith Taylor

FANFARE

And now: tulips
lush, in their oriental silks
(all the costliest dyestuffs)
when the flowers around them are spring-
muslin sprigs.

       I love their pride,
how it rears their gorgeous heads.
I love the dark
heart in their tiger colours,

how their heavy glamour folds itself
against the bitter night winds.
And I love

how they become themselves
most flagrantly in the face of death:

how they curl
open, arched, writhing, everything
on display

       a bared
double-meaning, the full
Elizabethan, and their silks
(paper-thin by now, and tattering)

still luscious as they shed them
one by one, to expose the core
sex.

How they go down
(I mean that as it sounds) in all their bravery
and in the dark
remake themselves, ready
                    to come again.

RESURRECTION

We buried the double-faced god
for a thousand years
not thinking how the earth, his friend
would preserve him
to stand again
in this museum doorway

his stone hands
clenched at his sides
his horns casting their fearful shadow
just as they did before
his centuries of abandonment.

The face he turned towards us
as we covered him up
is almost gone,
scraped and scored by the deep
-ploughing and -cutting machines
that brought him back to light:

the bridge of the nose, one eyesocket
all that's left. A lost look
wounded, almost querulous,
through the scars left by our implements.

But the face we turned away,
towards the underworld
we had learned to consider Hell,
is much as it always was: the line of the lips
the hard line of the eyebrows
and the shadows under them

from which he looks on us
with everything he knows
about our loyalties
and with everything he has seen
through all the years of staring down
into the dark.

Jacqueline Thompson

SYCORAX

I was a minnow of a girl, tossed
by the storm. Banished from Algiers
with the skin of my belly tight
as a drum, packed with the kicks
of my Caliban, whose diabolic
father knew a trick or two.

Many moons rose. I wove an eel-
grass cradle, chased mischievous
spirits from my driftwood door.
Waves curling behind me like claws,
I screamed him out. Beneath a squid-
ink sky he hit the sand as lightning struck.

I loved my moon-calf dear, stroked
the bristles on his cheeks, caressed
his crooked spine. I held him high
to pick our olives, figs and oranges
until my salty breath ran out
and I became pure essence.

Prospero offered my boy stolen fruit
on open palms, beguiled with wily
spells. Now Caliban bears wood
like a mule, weeps over his chains
until iron turns to rust and man
turns to beast with a poet's tongue.

Ah, his words might be as sweet
as peaches. At night, he rocks
gently, sings lullabies; but they are

few, and brief, and soiled with curses.
Oh, he could be so tall if he would
only walk with unbowed spine.

Colin Will

INK

Pain is the wrong word. That was the first thing I found out. I suppose I'd got myself worked up beforehand, knowing how hypodermic needles feel, knowing how I react to cuts, to blood. But there was no blood. And the needles didn't really penetrate to any depth, just enough to make an opening for the ink to stain the deeper levels of dead skin cells. I couldn't call this feeling 'pain'.

We talked. The whole time. We talked. I know it's a thing with me, I like talking to women, everybody knows that. There's no harm in it, no hidden agenda. I'm a man. I'm a man who likes women. And when this young woman's attention is focused on me, there's no question but that we have a most potent and intimate connection. She has designs on my body.

The concept first hit me as an abstract idea, until I had a picture of it in my head: an open book. I write, I have been published, I have published many others; books were my life for nearly forty years. So a book was natural, fitting. Open fits too. I hide nothing, except for my most secret thoughts, my machinations – I do have some – and maybe my weirdnesses – I have a few of those too. But mostly I hold up a piece of plain glass to the world. This is me, I say, what you see is what you get. Take me as I am, I am all surface. I have no hidden depths. I am skin deep. This is it.

So, she worked away on paper, showed it to me. I liked it. An open book, a symbol of me at my most naked, the skin I show the world. Where did I want it? Below the right shoulder, nothing flagrant, nothing flashy, no flashing. Concealment, but not really hidden. I could show this to those who wanted to see it. And many did, that first night.

She transferred the design to my skin, my outer integument, the epidermis, below the same shoulder I'd done so much work on, so much physio after three years of pain. All the rotator-cuff strengthening had, I was sure, decalcified the tendon, allowed it to stretch again, to pull its weight through the tunnel of forces and vectors in that complex arthritic joint, an almost normal range of arm movements. Now pain was only an occasional twinge, not every night, not every turn of the body on to the right side.

We talked. She told me about the places she'd visited with her boyfriend. I'd been to some of them too, and we smiled at our separate memories. I told her about some other places I thought she'd like. We talked about my writing: the poetry and short stories, the gig I was reading at that evening. She didn't know anything about the literary world, but she kept me talking, kept me listening; this was definitely a two-way conversation. I told her I'd been born in Tollcross, this part of the city, the street behind the King's Theatre, and my grandparents stayed on the same street as the tattoo parlour. The time ran by most pleasantly, and I was distracted, I'm sure intentionally, from the thought of what she was doing to my arm with the needles and inks in that buzzing machine.

And then it was over. She put on a patch of clingfilm, told me about aftercare, and I thanked her with a warm handshake. I know she'd provided a service I paid for, but for me it was so much more. She had fulfilled one of my ambitions, like the guy in the music shop who sold me a tenor sax. She had made one of my dreams come true. I'd had an itch, and she scratched it.

John Young

MA WEE BUIK O GENESIS

Chapter 1: Creation

Michty, whit a week this has been whit wi aw that creatin I've been daein. The furst couplae days wirnae too bad, jist pairtin the licht fae the dark, dividin the land fae the watters an settin up the firmament – bittae a dawdle fur a chiel o ma talents, bit the last twa or three days taxed me sair. Wha'd ha thocht that there'd hae been sae muckle darg in populatin the earth wi sae mony craeturs – beasts o the field, fowls o the air, fishes o the sea, an even thae wee creepy crawlies that buzz aboot aw-whair, stingin an bitin, jist tae git oan yer nerves. An the variety, it's fair taen ma breith awa, surprised even masel.

Truth is, I was fair forfochten eftir pittin thegither aw thae heids an boadies, airms an legs, hoofs an horns, an fin, flipper an feather whaur needit. It wis in guid hert that I stertit the work, tackin tent o wheethir I should gie a craetur lang legs or short ains, lungs or gills, wheethir a wooly coat or a braw sleekit jaickit suited tae the life it'd lead. Bit as the day wore oan, an there seemed tae be nae end o pairts tae be fitted, I stertit tae lose ma concentration. Sae I fun masel stickin humps oan some desert craeturs, whiles ae hump, whiles twa. An I endit up pittin lang nebs wi nostrils like fingers oan some lumberin brutes wi skinny wee tails, an teeny wee wings oan glaikit luckin burds that cud only rin aboot peckin at stanes an hidin thir heids in the sand.

Gittin fair scunnered near the end o the day I set tae mackin a virtue o necessity an hit oan the idea o pittin the skeleton oan the outside an no the inside – sey abracadabra, thair's a lobster, Hey Presto, thair's a crab, an syne jist stickin wee shells oan the backs o rubbery wee crawlers aboot, fur I had faur too mony shells left ower eftir I'd creatit aw the shore life.

Hardest tae dae though wis ma last bit o work. I'm no really fu o masel bit I thocht that I cud mibbe dae somethin in ma ain image, sae I cam up wi the idea o a twa legged craetur wha hadnae

muckle sense o whit he wis or whit his purpose in the warl micht
be. Tae help him oot I gied him a wife, jist tae keep him richt
ye ken – fur withoot his mate wha kens whit kind o a bourach
he'd mak o things? Aye, I'd taen wan o his ribs an shaped it intae
the bonniest craetur ye'd ever clapped yer een oan. An I pit them
tae bide in a gairden whaur they'd find aw they needit: they wir ma
pride an joy.

Chapter 2: Paradise Lost

I tellt them, I tellt them, they had nae excuse for it for I'd tellt them,
Jist dinnae touch onything fae that tree o knowledge an ye'll be awricht!
but naw, naw, curiosity killt mair nor the cat, an the wife jist hud
tae hae a bite o that aipple an then inveigle her man, daft gowk for
listenin tae her, in aw the stramash that follayed. He coulda refused,
bit eejit that he is, he jist went an had a bite o it oneywey.

I micht no ha kent, like, bit thair they wir, jist plitterin aboot in
the gairden wi nae claes oan, jist as ye'd expect, no even a semmit
atween them but kina reid-faced an hingin luggit, wi big leaves
strung aroon thir hurdies, an they couldnae wait tae tell me whit
wrang they'd done. *It wis the snake* she said *that tellt me tae dae it.*
Oh aye, says I, an hud the snake tellt ye tae loup intae the river, wud
ye hae done that anaw? Aye, ma dander wis up, an I wis lourin a bit
an gittin gey crabbit, mair aboot that snake nor aboot the man an
wife, fur they wir in ma image an I hud a saft spot fur thaim. Sae
when I goat a huddae that snake I left him in nae twa minds, *Fae
noo oan ye slink aboot oan yer wame,* says I, *an ye'll git nae favours
fae man nor fae me.*

But I still hud tae pey the man an wife thir dues, gie them thir
licks kinna thing, so I says in as maisterfu a voice as I cud muster,
*Ye've done an awfu thing, wantin tae ken aboot awthing, an whit tae
dae wi yer . . . danglin bits an aw that . . .* I wis gittin fair fashed sae
I cam richt tae the pint, *Ye wanted tae ken aw aboot the warl, sae
noo's yir chance – yir oot, an tae mak shair ye'll no come back I'm
pittin a squad o cherubim oan guard at aw the gates tae keep ye oot.*

An then I thocht, puir sowels oot thair in the cauld, sae I gied
them some claes afore they left, an a word o advice. *Tak tent* says I

tae the man, *think weel on whit ye've done the day, an dinnae pey attention tae aw yer wife says; be the maister o yer ain hoose,* an giein a bit o a wink tae the wife when he turns awaw, I says, *An mibbe* **you've** *learnt hoo tae git yer man tae dae whit* **you** *want, bit bear in mind that gittin yer ain wey micht no ay be the best thing fur ye.*

Chapter 3: The Flood

I'm no shair I goat that richt at aw, aw that trauchle wi a flood an Noah wi his muckle boat, an stertin oot again tae mak a new warl. Naw I michta goat it wrang. Mair aboot ma choosin Noah than oneything else I'm kickin masel: tae see him stotterin aboot that vineyard o his noo, forevvir fu oan that wine o his; him yet livin whaur aw the ither folk are deid – bi the deluge I'd sent!

An thair's the nub o't: I hud them aw drooned fur I wis fair scunnered bi thir bousin an carousing an fechtin amang thirsels, an it vexes me tae say it – thir hoorin. No a day gawin by but they're fornicatin like rabbits, or yon monkeys up trees, or . . . or, och I'll need tae sit doon, I'm fair rinnin ootae words at the thocht o't. Bit it wisnae jist hoo the folk wir cairryin oan wi each ither that led me tae dae awaw wi them aw; it wis mair tae dae wi thir no tackin tent o me in oney wey – me, the ane wha'd creatit them aw, gien them the braith o life, an wrocht them in ma ain image.

The ane yin amang them that had gied me due respect wis that Noah, him an his three laddies, Ham, Shem an Japheth. Sae I made a deal wi them, a covenant, fur thaim tae bigg a boat tae ma exact spec, an tae bring aw the beasties intae it, twa bi twa, tae replenish the warl eftir I'd laid it waste. An tae be fair, aw that went tae plan. It brocht pleeshir tae me an credit tae thaim hoo Noah an his faimly haunled the business o luckin eftir aw the craeturs o the Earth while I let the rain stote doon fur forty days an forty nichts, till they wir aw drookit an then drooned, aw they malefactors.

It wis when the floods eased aff though that I stertit tae hae ma doots aboot Noah an his drunkenness, comin tae a heid whan his laddies fun him in his tent ae nicht. Drunk tae the warl, wi nae claes oan – no the role model I'd hud in mind fur the future. Hud I pickt the richt chiel tae dae ma biddin? Mibbe naw, bit hoo cud I git ootae ma covenant? I'd tellt him I'd luk eftir him, an I'd brocht forth yon braw watergaw as a symbol o ma guid intent – hoo cud I gie him a sherrickin eftir that?

Weel, I'll keep ma ain council the noo, bit there'll be nae mair o lettin men live fur seevin or eicht hunder year – Noah'll be the last – mibbe jist a hunder or a hunder an twinty fae noo oan; an I'll tak it oot oan Noah's faimly through that halflin, Canaan, Ham's laddie, wha seems tae hae taen eftir his faither as a bit o a radical.

Chapter 4: The Tower of Babel (*vox pop*)

How vindictive was that!
God sends a great flood
To wipe out mankind.
He fails. We survive –

So coming together
From all the known world
We agree to show
What, given the chance,
We can achieve.

We set to work
Erecting a skyscraper
That should reach up
Right to the heavens.

But God, in his wisdom,
Sees this as a threat
And he works out a plan
To confuse and confound us;
Making our joint endeavour
So much harder to complete.

By taking away
Our common tongue
And creating 72

New languages
He breeds misunderstanding,
Suspicion and dissent
Among us.

We abandon the project.

Oz gna storblic zedquelledan
Erf jaxtof potibolistica
Na midgle yamardale
Coosflaxer se etnad

Chapter 5: Abraham

Noo I ken the story's a bit confusin an that he didnae ay play the gemme wi ither kings an chiefs an high heid yins, an whiles no even wi his wife. Bit he wis the best I cud find tae pin ma hopes oan. Eftir no gettin it quite richt wi Noah, an aw that stramash ower the tooer o Babel, I jist needed somebody, oneybody, that wis hauf decent, tae stert aff a model nation – tae be the faither o ma chosen people. Sae, mair in hope nor expectation, I lichtit oan tae Abraham.

Fae the stert I cud see his fauts, mairryin his hauf sister, no the thing tae dae in ma rule buik, an twice no letting oan she wis his wife an haundin her ower tae ither men tae save his ain skin. Bit he wis the ane amang them aw I cud rely oan tae be ma faithful servant, ay ready tae gie me a burnt oafferin or tae seek oot ma coonsel whenivver he goat intae oney bother: he wis the ane I dependit oan. An he wis guid-hertit – like yon time when I tellt him I wis set oan wreackin hellfire an damnation oan Sodom and Gomorrah, they cesspits o corruption, he goat doon oan his knees an pleaded wi me tae spare his nephew, Lot, wha bided in ane o they toons.

I wis fur burnin them aw, man wumman an bairn, fur they had vexed me sair wi thir loose livin, thir perversions, thir interferin wi aw kin o craeturs, thir wanton deviations baith wi the quick an the deid, thir nivver-endin houghmagandie. Bit it wis Abraham that persuaded me tae save Lot an his kith an kin. An that faimly wis aw spared barrin that feckless wife o Lot's wha hud tae turn her heid back tae gawk at the destruction I'd wrocht. I turned her intae a pillar o saut fir that, bit that's anither story.

Favourin Abraham as I did (I goat tae cawin him Abe), even yet, I hud tae keep oan testin him. No that I'm a skeptic nor oneything like that, I jist hud tae be shair that I'd goat the richt man this time. Sae I tellt him, *That laddie o yours, that Isaac that's jist turned thirteen, tak him tae a place I'll pint oot tae ye, an oaffer him up thair as a sacrifice tae me. That's richt* says I when I sees him gittin kinna pale roon the gills, *a burnt oafferin o yir laddie.* Weel I thocht he michta pit up some kinna protest, but naw, he jist nodded an the twa o them set oaff, him wi a knife in his haun, an young Isaac cairryin a bundle o wid. When they goat tae the place I hud in mind the boy speirs o his faither as tae whaur the lamb micht be. His faither says, 'God will provide,' an gars him lie doon tae be trussed up like a bubblyjock fur the oven. Syne, jist whan he's aboot tae stick the knife in the loon I order ane o ma angels tae stey his haun, an shew him a ram trammelled up in some brambles tae be yaised as a sacrifice insteed o the laddie.

I tell ye this tae shew ye that I'm a mercifu God, an tae mak crystal clear whye I chose Abraham tae be the patriarch o my peoples acroass the length an breidth o the land.

Chapter 6: The rest o Genesis

I kinna stude back a wee eftir settin Abraham oan the richt road: no interferin sae much wi the folk, bit ay lourin doon through the cloods fae time tae time, jist tae see hoo they wir mackin oot. Mibbe I'd regretted that some o the maitters I'd hud a pairt in hadnae turned oot sae muckle weel, an I thocht it michta been time fur thaim created in ma image tae tak oan mair responsibility fur thirsels, sae eftir the daith o Abraham I left them tae stravaig aboot the desert fur a generation or twa tae fecht amang thirsels an wi ither clans fae aw roon aboot.

Whit I mean is that wi things like the flood an the tooer o Babel, the layin waste o Sodom an Gomorrah, an even the strife atween Cain an Abel lang syne, at the foond it wis me tackin offence that brocht aboot aw the daith an destruction, bit eftir Abraham an Isaac

I left weel alane – fur a while at least. Sae the wey Jacob did Esau ootae his birthright an trickt his blin an doannart auld faither intae giein him Esau's blessin wisnae at ma instigation; it wis aw tae dae wi thir mither favourin ane brither ower the ither. Nae mair wis it ma faut that Joseph fell oot wi his faimly an held them tae ransom doon in Egypt.

Ye see, I minded aboot yon furst deception in the gairden, when aw they cud think aboot wis knowledge, an daein whit they wanted tae dae mair than whit I wanted them tae dae. Sae it cam aboot that, fur a while oneyweys, I left them tae mak a kirk or a mill o't – an if ye read ma big book o Genesis ye'll see they made mair a mill nor a kirk.

BIOGRAPHIES

Viccy Adams is an Edinburgh-based writer. Her short fiction has been widely published in anthologies and online zines, and her creative non-fiction collection, *There & Now: a writer's perspective on life in South West China*, was published by Cargo in 2015. She tweets **@ViccyIsWriting** and blogs **www.viccyadams.com**.

Jane Aldous won the Wigtown Poetry Competition in 2012 and her poems have been commended in the Norman MacCaig Centenary Poetry Competition, the Baker Prize and the Manchester Writing for Children Prize. She has also had poems published in *Northwords Now, Southlight, The Eildon Tree* and *poetandgeek*.

Jennifer M. Baker was brought up in Glasgow and taught English before moving to the island of Lismore where she has a tiny business growing lavender and keeping bees. She has written for *TESS, History Scotland* and educational journals. Writing fiction is much more fun. *A Hebridean Collection* is nearly finished.

Henry Bell is a writer and editor from Bristol, working on poetry and theatre. He lives on the south side of Glasgow and edits *Gutter* magazine. He was a Clydebuilt poet and has edited books including *A Bird is Not a Stone*. You can find out more at **henryjimbell.com** or **@henbell**.

Lynsey Calderwood comes from a family who like to talk, yet seldom read books, and never write anything down. She broke tradition by publishing a memoir in 2002, and has since gallivanted into fiction.

Jim Carruth is the current Glasgow Poet Laureate. His first full collection *Killochries*, published in 2015, was shortlisted for the Saltire Scottish Poetry Book of the Year and the Seamus Heaney Centre for Poetry Prize. His most recent collection, *Black Cart*, was published in 2017.

Landscape and sense of place are central to **Linda Cracknell**'s work in both fiction and non-fiction. Her last two published books have been a novel, *Call of the Undertow*, featuring a cartographer, and a book of essays, *Doubling Back: Ten paths trodden in memory*. Linda lives in Highland Perthshire. **www.lindacracknell.com**.

Anna Crowe is the co-founder and former Artistic Director of StAnza. Awards include the Peterloo Poetry Prize, a Travelling Scholarship from the Society of Authors, the Callum Macdonald Memorial Award and two PBS Choices. Her translations from Catalan and Castilian are published by Bloodaxe and Arc. Her poetry has been translated into several languages.

A working playwright, **Sylvia Dow** has had plays commissioned and produced by the Traverse Theatre, Stellar Quines, Greyscale Company, and Oran Mor amongst others, and is a member of playwright collectives Village Pub Theatre and Thrawn Craws. This is her first attempt at the short story form.

Louise Farquhar grew up in Dumfries and studied law at Glasgow University. When she's not chained to her desk she can be found in a library or coffee shop, or preferably a combination of the two. She lives in the leafy suburbs with her family and lots of books.

Graham Fulton has had eleven critically acclaimed books of poetry published, the most recent being *Brian Wilson in Swansea Bus Station* (Red Squirrel Press), *Paragraphs at the End of the World* (Penniless Press Publications) and *Equal Night* (Salmon Poetry). He was also co-author of *Pub Dogs of Glasgow* (Freight Books).

Gordon Gibson lives in Troon, South Ayrshire. Over the last seven years, his writing – prose fiction and poetry – has appeared in a number of print and online publications.

Mandy Haggith is a writer and environmental activist living in Assynt. Her poetry collections include *letting light in*, *Castings* and

A-B-Tree, a celebration of the Gaelic Tree Alphabet written while poet in residence at Edinburgh Royal Botanic Gardens. She also writes novels and plays. **www.mandyhaggith.net**.

Brian Hamill has lived in Glasgow since 2009. He currently works as a software developer, and serves as Submissions Editor for *thi wurd* magazine. Brian has had stories published in various books and magazines. He was a winner of the Scottish Book Trust New Writers Award, 2013.

Lydia Harris's first pamphlet, *Glad Not to be the Corpse,* was published by Smiths Knoll in 2012. She holds a Scottish Book Trust New Writer Award 2017 for poetry and lives in Westray, Orkney.

Sarah Isaac was born and brought up in Wales. After many years working as an art teacher, she is now completing a Masters degree in Creative Writing and Practice part-time at Dundee University. She has been shortlisted and longlisted in numerous competitions, including the Bristol Short Story prize.

Andy Jackson is author of two poetry collections, including *A Beginner's Guide to Cheating* (Red Squirrel, 2015), and editor of several anthologies, including *Whaleback City* (2013) and *Double Bill* (2014). He co-edited (with Brian Johnstone) the Scotia Extremis project and is Makar to the Federation of Writers Scotland for 2017.

Nadine Aisha Jassat (Nadine Aisha) is the author of *Still,* a debut poetry pamphlet, and has performed solo shows at the Edinburgh Fringe, Just and Audacious Women festivals. She is the Writer in Residence for YWCA Scotland – The Young Women's Movement – and features in 404 Ink's *Nasty Women*.

Brian Johnstone's work has appeared throughout Scotland, elsewhere in the UK, in Ireland, North America and Europe. He has published six collections, most recently *Dry Stone Work* (Arc, 2014), and his work appears on The Poetry Archive website. His memoir

Double Exposure was published by Saraband in February 2017. **brianjohnstonepoet.co.uk**.

Lis Lee trained as a journalist. Her poetry, drama and prose have appeared in various anthologies and journals, including *New Writing Scotland*. She lives and works in Kelso, in the Scottish Borders. Her most recent poetry collection was *Vanilla Summer*, published by Dionysia Press, Edinburgh.

Wes Lee currently lives in New Zealand with her Scottish partner. Her poems have appeared in *New Writing Dundee*, *The London Magazine*, *Poetry London*, and many other journals. She has won a number of awards for her writing, including the BNZ Katherine Mansfield Literary Award. Her publications include *Cowboy Genes* (Grist Books, 2014) and *Shooting Gallery* (Steele Roberts, 2016).

Joan Lennon is a Canadian Scot, who lives and writes in a flat overlooking Dundee and the silvery River Tay. She has had novels, stories and poems published for readers of all ages. Her latest YA novel, *Silver Skin*, is set in Skara Brae, Orkney.

Robin Lloyd-Jones is an award-wining author who writes both fiction and non-fiction, the former being historical novels and the latter mainly on travel and environmental topics. Robin, a former president of Scottish PEN International, lives in Helensburgh. He is currently researching into creativity in later life. **www.robinlloydjones.com**.

Rose McDonagh was born in Edinburgh. She has had work published in *BBC WildLife Magazine*, *SmokeLong Quarterly*, *Labyrinth/Orange*, *Fairfield Review*, the *Guardian* online, *The Eildon Tree*, *Brittle Star* and *Gutter*. She has also been a guest blogger for *Mslexia*. Her agent is Sarah Williams. She is on Twitter **@rose_mcdonagh**.

Ian McDonough was brought up in Brora on the east coast of Sutherland. He has published four collections of poetry, most recently

A Witch Among The Gooseberries, published by Mariscat in 2014. His work has appeared widely, including *Poetry Review*, *Times Educational Supplement*, *Physics Review* and *The Scotsman*.

Alan Macfarlane is a Humanities graduate living in the Central Belt. Having recently become study-free, he has been dusting off his notebooks and finally dedicating time to doing something with the scribblings inside them. Alan is a poet, but one who is also keen to scratch a short-fiction itch.

Rachael McGill was born in Shetland. She lives with one foot in Britain, the other in Lisbon. She's a professional playwright and has recently finished a novel. Fiction has been published in *The Asham Award* anthology, the *Macallan/Scotland on Sunday Short Story Collection*, *Frogmore Papers* and online.

James McGonigal is a poet and biographer, currently working on Edwin Morgan's uncollected translations and his writings about translation. His prize-winning pamphlets include *Passage/An Pasaíste* (2004) and *Cloud Pibroch* (2010), and his recent collection is *The Camphill Wren* (Red Squirrel Press, 2016).

Brought up in Glasgow, **Roddie McKenzie** worked as a molecular biologist and lecturer in the UK and overseas. He continues to be a member of Nethergate Writers in Dundee, where he learned creative writing. He is working on a novel. His poems and short stories are online and in print.

Hugh McMillan is a poet from Dumfries and Galloway in Scotland. He has won several awards and is widely published and anthologised. His selected poems, *Not Actually being in Dumfries*, was published by Luath in 2015.

David McVey lectures at New College Lanarkshire. He has published over 120 short stories (including 'The D Row' in *New Writing Scotland* 26) and lots of non-fiction that focuses on history and the outdoors.

He enjoys hillwalking, visiting historic sites, reading, watching telly, and supporting Kirkintilloch Rob Roy FC.

Laura Morgan is published in *The Moth, Causeway/Cabhsair, Northwords Now, Words from an Island, Hysteria 5*, and *The Bottle Imp*. She is currently a recipient of the Scottish Book Trust New Writer Award, which she is using to complete her first short story collection, *Winter Ground*. She blogs at **aremoteview. wordpress.com**.

Mairi Murphy graduated with a Masters in Creative Writing from Glasgow University and was awarded the 2016 Alistair Buchan Prize for poetry. Published in *New Writing Scotland 30, From Glasgow to Saturn, Shetland Create* and *Crooked Holster*, she is editor of *Glasgow Women Poets*, published by Four-em Press, which she co-founded.

Andrew Neilson was born in Edinburgh in 1975. His poetry has recently appeared in *The Dark Horse* and the *Glasgow Review of Books*, while his fiction has been published in *Short Fiction* 8 and 10. He lives and works in London.

Niall O'Gallagher is the author of two poetry collections, *Beatha Ùr* (Clàr, 2013) and *Suain nan Trì Latha* (Clàr, 2016). A selected volume, with Irish translations by Eoghan Mac Giolla Bhríde, is forthcoming from Éabhlóid. His opposition to translating his own poems is outlined in 'Sealg Dealain-dè', recently published in *STEALL*.

Catherine Ogston has lived in Edinburgh and South Africa, and briefly in Israel and Berkshire, before returning to Perthshire. She has placed in various local writing groups competitions in the last five years and in a number of Scottish Association of Writers contests. In between teaching she enjoys writing with Perthshire Writers.

Heather Parry is an Edinburgh-based writer and editor. She won the 2016 Bridge Award for an Emerging Writer, and has been published in several magazines, including *The Stinging Fly*. She performed her work at the 2016 Edinburgh International Book Festival and is currently working on her first novel.

Rachel Plummer is a poet living in Edinburgh with her partner and two young children. She has had poems in magazines including *Mslexia*, *The Dark Horse* and *Agenda*. She is a recipient of the Scottish Book Trust New Writers Award for poetry. Find her at **www.rachelplummer.co.uk**.

Sharon Gunason Pottinger was born in Chicago and worked as a technical writer until moving to the far north of Scotland in 2005 provided the opportunity to write fiction, poetry and essays in the local papers. Her debut novel, *Returning: The Journey of Alexander Sinclair*, was published in 2015.

Julie Robertson is an artist and art tutor at Strathclyde University. She comes from a Glasgow Irish family where storytelling came with the blood. The older generation are gone but she likes to think that she continues that tradition with her writing. No existential thought in her stories but hopefully narratives laced with wit and mischief.

Cynthia Rogerson has written five novels and a collection of stories. Her work has been translated, shortlisted for Scottish Novel of the Year and serialised for Woman's Hour. She won the V. S. Pritchett Prize. *Wait for Me Jack* is published under her pen name, Addison Jones. Californian, she's lived in Scotland for over thirty-five years.

Helen Sedgwick is the author of *The Comet Seekers* (Harvill Secker, 2016) and *The Growing Season* (Harvill Secker, 2017). Her debut has been published in seven countries and selected as a Best Book of 2016 by the *Herald* and *Glamour*. Before becoming a writer, she worked as a research physicist.

Harry Smart grew up in Leeds and lives in Montrose. He published three collections of poetry with Faber – *Pierrot*, *Shoah* and *Fool's Pardon* – and a novel, *Zaire*, with Dedalus. He is writing a novel, *The Blue Poppy*, and a theology of violence for unbelievers, called *Violence in the Heart*.

Graeme Stones was a professional diver for a decade and then, misguidedly, a teacher. He escaped to an island on the west coast, mends boats, tends sheep and writes in-between.

Judith Taylor lives and works in Aberdeen. Her poetry has been published widely in magazines, and in two pamphlet collections – *Earthlight* (Koo Press, 2006) and *Local Colour* (Calder Wood Press, 2010). Her first full-length collection, *Not in Nightingale Country*, will be published in Autumn 2017 by Red Squirrel Press.

Jacqueline Thompson has a Creative Writing PhD from the University of Edinburgh. Her poems have appeared in *The Scotsman*, *Gutter* and *Poetry Ireland Review*. She has been shortlisted for the Grierson Verse Prize, the Westport Arts Festival Poetry Prize, the Melita Hume Poetry Prize and the Jane Martin Poetry Prize.

Colin Will is a Dunbar-based poet, short story writer and musician. He has chaired the boards of the Scottish Poetry Library and the StAnza Festival. He's had eight poetry collections published and one short story pamphlet (*Getting On*, Postbox Press, 2016). He plays saxophones and clarinets. **www.colinwill.co.uk**.

John Young was born in Edinburgh in 1942. He was brought up mainly in Leith but has lived and worked in Newcastle-upon-Tyne, Corby and Milan. Most of his working life has been in education, but he has had a variety of other employments. He recently retired from his post as an adult education organiser.